A Short Introduction to
STATA FOR BIOSTATISTICS
Updated to Stata 12

TIMBERLAKE
Statistics · Econometrics · Forecasting

www.**timberlake**.co.uk
www.**timberlake-consultancy**.com

A Short Introduction to
STATA FOR BIOSTATISTICS
Updated to Stata 12

Michael Hills
Bianca L. De Stavola

Published by Timberlake Consultants Ltd.
A Leading Distributor of Statistical and Econometrics Software

A Short Introduction to Stata for Biostatistics – Updated to Stata 12
Copyright @ 2012 Michael Hills and Bianca L. De Stavola
First published in 2002. Revised in 2003, 2006, 2007, 2009, 2012.

British Library Cataloguing-in-Publication Data
A catalogue record for this book is available from the British Library

Library of Congress Cataloguing-in-Publication Data
A catalogue record of this book is available from the Library of Congress
Michael Hills and Bianca L. De Stavola
p. cm. – (A Short Introduction to Stata for Biostatistics – updated to Stata 12)

ISBN 978-0-9571708-0-3

Published by:
Timberlake Consultants Ltd
Unit B3, Broomsleigh Business Park, Worsley Bridge Road, London SE26 5BN, U.K.
http://www.timberlake.co.uk

842 Greenwich Lane,
Union, NJ 07083-7905, U.S.A.
http://www.timberlake-consultancy.com

Preface

Starting to use Stata is relatively simple, but because of its size, and the wealth of information in the documentation, the question of what comes next can be rather daunting. This book provides a short introduction which will help answer this question. Although written with biostatisticians in mind, much of the material in the book is equally relevant to other disciplines.

We believe that the only way to learn Stata is to try it out, so we assume that the reader is seated in front of a computer which is running Stata. For this reason we have not felt it necessary to print the output which follows Stata commands. Of course there are occasions when it is reassuring to see that the output on the screen is the same as the output on the page, and we occasionally include some output for this reason, but the spirit of the book is to try something and see what happens. In keeping with this we have not provided solutions to the exercises, but instead a program produces the solutions on the screen.

We have mostly used official Stata commands but, as one of the features of Stata is the large number of user written commands, we have also felt free to use a few of these, where appropriate. In particular, Chapters 10 – 12 depend on two commands, written specifically for this book, which provide dialog boxes for making tables and estimating effects. The ideas in these chapters arose from courses taught jointly by Michael Hills and David Clayton, and we gratefully acknowledge David's contribution.

The data sets and additional program files are an integral part of the book. They are included on the CD-ROM which comes with the book, but are also available as a download from *www.timberlake.co.uk*. Instructions on how to proceed with each of these media are given in Chapter 0: Getting Started.

Michael Hills, Retired
email: *mhills@blueyonder.co.uk*

Bianca De Stavola, London School of Hygiene and Tropical Medicine
email: *bianca.destavola@lshtm.ac.uk*

January 23, 2012

Contents

Chapter 0

Getting started

The book is written under the assumption that the user will be using Microsoft Windows, so some of the specifics will be different for users on other operating systems. Start Stata 12 by clicking on the Stata icon and you will see a large window for results together with four smaller windows labelled *Review*, *Variables*, *Properties* and *Command*. The working directory, shown at the bottom left hand side of the screen, is the directory where Stata expects to find the data when no path is specified. It will be

`C:\Users\Username\Documents`

when users wish to keep separate folders for their working directory, and `C:\data` when all users use the same folder. We shall assume it is `C:\data`. The default colour scheme is black on a white background, but alternative schemes can be found by right-clicking in the results window and selecting preferences.

Typing and editing commands

Below the results screen there is the *Command* window for typing Stata commands. When doing this remember that Stata is case sensitive, so 'A' is not the same as 'a'. To edit a previously run command, click on it in the review window, or use the Page-Up key to retrieve the previous command line, then modify it in the command window, as required. Several commands can be copied together from the review window and pasted in the command window, or you can select each in turn and double click on it.

Stata prompt

When a command is executed it will appear in the results window with a dot in front. The dot is there to distinguish between commands and results, and is referred to as the Stata prompt. In this book we shall indicate those commands which you need to

1

type into the command window by starting them with a Stata prompt. You should not type the prompt - only the command. For example,

```
. describe
```

means you should type describe in the command window.

Files for the book

An integral part of the book is a set of data files and programs, which need to be installed in a convenient folder. For Microsoft Windows users we suggest making a folder **hs** within the **data** folder. This can be done by starting Stata, selecting the *File* tab, then *Change Working Directory*. In the resulting screen, highlight the *data* folder, click on *Make New Directory*, and then enter **hs** without clicking. Press *OK* and the working directory will now be

```
C:\data\hs
```

shown in the bottom left hand side of the screen.

The files on the CD-ROM are arranged in two packages: hsbook for data sets and programs written specially for the book, and **userfiles** for programs written by users and referred to in the book. To load these packages, type the following commands in the command window

```
. net from D:\
. net install hsbook
. net install userfiles
. net get hsbook
```

This will install the program files and put the data files in the **hs** directory. On some PC's the CD-ROM is referred to by another letter, such as E, instead of D. Watch out for error messages. If files with the same names have already been installed, and their content is different from that of the files on the CD-ROM, Stata will display an error message and will not install the new files. To over-write the old files with the new files you need to type

```
. net install hsbook, replace
. net install userfiles, replace
. net get hsbook, replace
```

To download the files from the Timberlake website, start Stata and type the following commands in the command window:

```
. net from http://www.timberlake.co.uk/data/hs12/
. net install hsbook
. net install userfiles
. net get hsbook
```

To download the version of the files for Stata 11, use the directory `hs11` in place of `hs12`.

Stata under Unix or Macintosh

If you are running Stata under Unix or Macintosh you need to change these instructions to refer to the working directory and CD-ROM under the Operating System you are using.

Fonts

The default font for each of the Stata windows can be changed. To change the font for the results window when using Microsoft Windows, right click anywhere in the Stata results window and select *Font*. This will bring up a menu which allows you to increase or decrease the size of the font, and also to change the font style.

Updating your version of Stata

Stata is not supplied with this book, and you may be using a version which is older than the most recent one. It is important to keep your version up-to-date, and this is easily done if you have an internet connection. Simply enter

```
. update all
```

in the command window and then follow the instructions.

Getting out of Stata

Select the *File* tab on the top of the screen and then select *Exit*. If you have made changes to the data currently in memory, you will be asked whether you want to save changes before closing. Select *don't save*, unless you really want to over-write the file on disk - generally a very bad idea.

How to read this book

The book is meant to be read while sitting in front of a computer running Stata 12. Comments about a command generally come before the command, but sometimes a few words of explanation will follow, so it is always worth checking the next line of text when something unexpected happens. Try to avoid the temptation to hop from one Stata command to the next – the words between can be important! It is worth working through both Chapter 1 and Chapter 2, even though they cover the same material. Chapter 1 asks you to type commands in the command window, and Chapter 2 uses menus and dialog boxes. Working through both chapters will give you a good idea of the strengths and weaknesses of the two approaches.

Chapter 1

Some basic commands

This chapter introduces the `births` data and some of the basic Stata commands which are used regularly.

1.1 The births data

Variable	Units or Coding	Type	Name
Identity number	–	categorical	`id`
Birth weight	grams	metric	`bweight`
Birth weight < 2500 g	1=yes, 0=no	categorical	`lowbw`
Gestational period	weeks	metric	`gestwks`
Gestational period < 37 weeks	1=yes, 0=no	categorical	`preterm`
Maternal age	years	metric	`matage`
Maternal hypertension	1=hypertensive, 0=normal	categorical	`hyp`
Sex of baby (numeric)	1=male, 2=female	categorical	`sex`
Sex of baby (alphabetic)	male, female	categorical	`sexalph`

Table 1.1: Variables in the births data set

To introduce Stata we use the births data which concerns 500 mothers who had singleton births in a large London hospital. Some of the variables in this file are categorical, taking different categories as values; others are metric taking measurements as values. In general it is better to code categories numerically, but in order to demonstrate some features of Stata the sex of the baby is coded using numbers in the variable `sex` and using alphabetical characters in the variable `sexalph`. A sequence of characters such as "male" or "year 1990" is called a *string* and variables that hold such characters are called *string variables*. Variables that hold numerical data are called *numeric variables*. In the births data `sex` is a numeric variable while `sexalph` is a string variable.

1.2   A first look at the data

In the births file each observation contains the values of the variables for one of the 500 mothers.. To load the data, first check your working directory with the command

. cd

This should return one of

C:\data
C:\Users\Username\Documents

To change your working directory to `hs` (or whatever name you choose) type

. cd hs

You will need to do this every time you start Stata, because Stata opens in the default working directory. Now type

. use births

The results window will show this command followed by its results, in this case the label of the data set. The review window will also show the command for future reference. If you get the error message 'file births.dta not found' it means one of two things: either you have not loaded the files from the CD correctly, or you have not set the working directory correctly. You can check which files are actually in the working directory with the command

. dir

Once you have successfully loaded the births data you can browse its content by clicking on the *Data Editor (Browse)* icon (the icons at the top of the screen display their names when the mouse arrow rests on them without clicking), or typing

. browse

in the command window. You can see the names of the variables in the variables window, but a more informative way of doing this is by typing

. describe

in the command window. A good way to start an analysis is to ask for a summary of the data by typing

. summarize

This will produce the mean, standard deviation, and range, for each variable in turn, provided it is not a string variable. For string variables the summary is left blank. For a more detailed summary of the variable gestwks try

```
. summarize gestwks, detail
```

which lists the four smallest values and the four largest values, together with various summaries of the distribution. Listing the smallest and largest values is a useful check on data errors.

In most data there will be some missing values. These are usually coded using an isolated decimal point (.) in place of the value which is missing if the variable is numeric, or as blank ("") if the variable is string. If you wish to make a distinction between types of missingness, you can use up to 26 other missing values codes. These are .a, .b, .c, up to .z, and obey the order: first ., then .a, then .b, up to .z. The misstable command is useful for seeing whether there are missing values:

```
. misstable summarize
```

The output shows that there are 10 missing values for gestwks and preterm, all coded with an isolated decimal point. Another useful command for inspecting the values which variables take is codebook. Try

```
. codebook
. codebook gestwks
. codebook, compact
```

to see what codebook does. The list command is used to list the values in the data file. Try out the following and see the consequences:

```
. list matage
```

Stata stops after each screen of output. Click on the *Go* icon, or press the space-bar, to get another screen. Alternatively, press the *Enter* key to continue line by line. You can cancel this command (and any other Stata command) by clicking on *Break* (the red octagon at the top of the screen like a stop sign). Stata commands can be restricted to observations 1, 2, . . . , 5 (for example) by adding in 1/5 to the command. Try

```
. list matage in 1/5
. list matage bweight in 11/20
```

The command list with no variable names, will list the data for all the variables. For example,

```
. list in 1/5
```

lists all variables for observations 1–5. Depending on the width of your screen the data are listed either in a display or table style. You can however force one or the other by adding the relevant option to the command. Try them both to see the difference:

```
. list in 1/5, display
. list in 1/5, table
```

If you wish to remove all dividing lines, try

```
. list in 1/5, table clean
```

The observation number can be omitted by using the option `noobs`, as in

```
. list in 1/5, table noobs
```

1.3 Tables of frequencies

When starting to look at any new data the first step is to check that the values of the variables make sense and correspond to the codes defined in the coding schedule. For categorical variables this can be done by looking at one-way frequency tables and checking that only the specified codes occur. The frequencies of the values taken by the categorical variables `hyp` and `sex` can be viewed by typing

```
. tabulate hyp
. tabulate sex
```

Their cross-tabulation is obtained by typing

```
. tabulate hyp sex
```

Cross-tabulations are useful when checking for consistency. The basic output from a cross-tabulation reports frequencies only; to include relative frequencies (percentages) within rows and/or columns add the options `row` and `col` as in

```
. tabulate hyp sex, row
. tabulate hyp sex, col
```

If you wish to see only the percentages use the option `nofreq`. To include missing values use the option `missing`:

```
. tabulate preterm sex, missing
```

Don't forget to save typing by recalling commands, either by clicking on them in the review window or by using the Page-Up key.

1.4 Tables of means and other things

The command `tabulate` can also be useful for making simple tables of means and standard deviations by a categorical variable. For example, to obtain the mean and standard deviation of `bweight` separately by `sex`, try

```
. tabulate hyp, summarize(gestwks)
. tabulate hyp sex, summarize(gestwks)
```

The frequencies refer to the number of nonmissing observations in each cell of the table. To display only the mean values of `bweight` try

```
. tabulate hyp sex, summarize(gestwks) means
```

For more complex tables the command `table` is used. We start by reproducing the table of the mean of `gestwks` by `hyp` using `table`:

```
. table hyp, contents(count mean gestwks sd gestwks)
```

The first variable following the command name determines the rows of the table. The word `contents` refers to the contents of the cells of the table and is usually abbreviated to `c`. The words `count` (or `n`), `mean`, and `sd` are among the keywords which are recognized by the `table` command and each keyword is followed by a variable name. To make a table of the median and the lower and upper quartiles for `gestwks`, by `hyp`, try

```
. table hyp, c(count gestwks median gestwks p25 gestwks p75 gestwks)
```

hypertens	N(gestwks)	med(gestwks)	p25(gestwks)	p75(gestwks)
0	419	39.35	38.15	40.18
1	71	38.03	36.94	39.43

The column headed `N(gestwks)` refers to the number of nonmissing values of `gestwks` in the two rows of the table. As another example, using `n` instead of `count` and describing `gestwks` and `bweight`, try

```
. table hyp, c(n gestwks median gestwks n bweight mean bweight)
```

To make a two-way table showing the mean birth weight by `sex` and `hyp`, try

```
. table sex hyp, c(count mean bweight)
```

The first variable following the command is `sex`, and this determines the rows of the table. The second variable (`hyp`) determines the columns. If you want this separately by `preterm` try

```
. table sex hyp, c(count mean bweight) by(preterm)
```

The command `tabstat` is very useful for summarizing several numeric variables in the same table. For example, to produce a table showing the mean and standard deviation of birth weight, weeks of gestation and maternal age, try

8

```
. tabstat bweight gestwks matage, statistics(mean sd)
```

where `mean` and `sd` are two of several keywords that go with the option `statistics`. When the option `statistics` is not used mean values are given by default. To display the means and standard deviations in columns you can use the option `col(stat)`. If you want them separately by sex try,

```
. tabstat bweight gestwks matage, statistics(mean sd) by(sex)
```

1.5   Restricting the scope of commands

We have seen that Stata commands can be restricted to observations $1, 2, \ldots, 5$ (for example), by adding `in 1/5` to the command. Commands can also be restricted to operate only on observations which satisfy given conditions. The conditions are added to the command using `if` followed by a logical expression. An example of a logical expression is `bweight < 2000`. This can only be true or false. The expression would be false for a subject with a birth weight equal to 3000g. To restrict the command `list` to observations for which this condition is true, try

```
. list bweight if bweight < 2000
```

If the logical expression `bweight < 2000` is true the observation is listed, but not otherwise. Other useful logical expressions are `X == Y` for equal, `X <= Y` for less or equal, `X >= Y` for greater or equal, and `X != Y` for not equal. A common error is to use = in a logical expression instead of ==. This is wrong because `X = 1` asks Stata to assign the value 1 to the variable X while `X == 1` is a logical expression, which does not change the value of X.

A command that uses logical expressions is `count`. It is particularly useful when exploring data. For example

```
. count if bweight <= 2000 & sex == 1
```

counts the number of observations for which `bweight <= 2000` and `sex == 1`. Note that the symbol for 'logical and' in Stata is `&`. Similarly,

```
. count if bweight <= 2000 | bweight > 4000
```

will count the number of babies whose birth weight was either less than or equal to 2000 g or greater than 4000 g. The symbol for 'logical or' in Stata is |, which is usually at the left end of the bottom row of letters on your keyboard. It is indicated by a broken vertical line on the key.

1.6   Generating new variables

New variables are generated using the command `generate`. Try

```
. generate num1 = 1
. generate num2 = 2
. browse
```

The new variable `num1` takes the value 1 for all observations, while `num2` takes the value 2. New variables which are made up from old variables can also be produced with `generate`, together with the usual mathematical operations and functions:

$$+ \quad - \quad * \quad / \quad \verb|^| \quad \exp() \quad \ln() \quad \mathrm{sqrt}()$$

The sign $\verb|^|$ means 'to the power of', ln means natural logarithm, and sqrt means square root. Some examples are

```
. generate num3 = num1 + num2
. generate num4 = num1/num2
. generate logbw = ln(bweight)
. browse
```

The variable `logbw` is the natural logarithm of birth weight. Note that `ln` could have been replaced by `log` as Stata treats them as synonyms. Logs to base 10 are obtained with `log10( )`. To browse `bweight` and `logbw` on their own try

```
. browse bweight logbw
```

To change the values of `num1` the command `replace` is used, as in

```
. replace num1 = 7
. browse num1
```

or

```
. replace num1 = 35 if hyp == 1
. browse num1 hyp
```

1.7   Ordering, dropping and keeping

The command

```
. describe
```

shows the list of variables in their current order. To change this order so that `id` and `sex` come first, try

```
. order id sex
. describe
. browse
```

You will see that the order has changed in the browser as well as the variables window. Variables that are no longer useful can be dropped, e.g.

```
. drop num1 num2
```

will drop the variables `num1` and `num2`. The command

```
. drop if sex == 1
```

will drop all observations with `sex` = 1. The command `keep` does the opposite of `drop`, so that the command

```
. keep logbw
```

will drop all variables except for `logbw`. Once data are dropped there is no way of getting them back other than by re-loading the data with

```
. use births, clear
```

where `clear` gives permission for the memory to be cleared before the births data are re-loaded.

1.8   Sorting data

Stata can sort the observations in a file according to values (numeric or string) of a variable. The `sort` command creates a key which tells Stata commands the order in which the observations should be processed. Try the following:

```
. list id matage sex sexalph in 1/10
. sort matage
. list id matage sex sexalph in 1/10
```

The observations are now sorted in ascending order of maternal age. To sort on `id` within `matage` try

```
. sort matage id
. list id matage sex sexalph in 1/10
```

You will see that within each value of `matage` the observations are sorted in order of `id`. To sort on a string variable try

```
. sort sexalph
. list id matage sex sexalph
```

Note that `female` comes before `male` because `f` comes before `m` in the alphabet. To restore the original sort order, try

```
. sort id
```

11

1.9   Using Stata as a calculator

The `display` command can be used to carry out simple calculations. For example, the command

```
. display 2+2
. display 2^3
. display ln(10)
. display sqrt(25)
```

will display 4, 8, the natural logarithm of 10, and the square root of 25 respectively. Text can also be displayed as in

```
. display "The natural logarithm of 10 is  " ln(10)
```

Note that the text must be surrounded by the quotes symbol.

   Standard probability functions are readily available. For example, the probability below 1.96 in a standard normal (i.e. Gaussian) distribution is obtained with

```
. display normal(1.96)
```

while

```
. display 1 - normal(1.96)
```

will display the probability above 1.96. Similarly,

```
. display chi2(1,3.84)
. display chi2tail(1,3.84)
```

will display the probability below and above 3.84 in a chi-squared distribution on 1 degree of freedom. Try `help probfun` for a full list of available probability functions.

1.10   Shortcuts

Variable names can be abbreviated, as long as the abbreviation is unique. Try

```
. list id matage hyp gestwks in 1/10
. list id mat hy gest in 1/10
. list i m h g in 1/10
```

Also lists of variable names can be shortened if they are consecutive

```
. list id-gestwks in 1/10
. list i-g in 1/10
```

or if they share some unique initial letters:

```
. list se* in 1/10
```

where `se*` stands for "all variables with names starting with `se`".

Command names, as well as options within commands, can be abbreviated (with a few exceptions). Try

```
. sum matage
. l  matage in 1/10
. br matage
. tab sex
```

Note that `tab` is accepted as an abbreviation for `tabulate`, *not* for `table`, which must be typed in full.

1.11   Stata syntax

The word syntax here refers to the rules which govern how a Stata command is put together. The heart of any Stata command takes the form

$$command \quad varlist \quad if\_expression \quad in\_range, \quad options$$

For example, try

```
. list bweight hyp if sex==1 in 1/10, table noobs
```

The *command* is `list`, the *varlist* is `bweight hyp`, the *if_expression* is `if sex==1`, the *in_range* is `in 1/10`, and the *options* are `table noobs`. Adding weights to a Stata command will be covered in Chapter 7.

1.12   Using the Stata help facilities

If you type `help` followed by the name of a Stata command you will see the help file for that command. For example, try typing `help list`. One useful bit to look at is the line which shows the syntax:

```
list [varlist] [if] [in] [, options ]
```

Parts of the syntax which are not essential are shown inside square brackets [ ]. In Stata commands the options are always entered after a comma. The syntax for `list` shows that there are several options available. If you scroll down the help screen you will see that they are described under the heading *Options*. Looking further down you will find some of the common ways in which the command is used. You can also use the *Jump to* tab instead of scrolling.

Another sort of help available from the Stata screen is help on commands linked to particular operations. Cancel the current help screen, click on *Help*, and then on

Search. Enter the keyword *tables* to search on, and you will see a long list of Stata commands relevant to making tables. These start with official commands from Stata and then go on to commands which have been written by users and published in the *Stata Journal* (previously the *Stata Technical Bulletin*) as well as links to relevant published material. We shall return to commands written by users in Chapter 21.

In Stata 12 the reference manuals are available as pdf files. These can be accessed via the *Help* tab.

Exercises

1. Load the births data.

2. List the variables `bweight` and `hyp` for observations 20–25 inclusive.

3. Summarize all variables.

4. Summarize `matage` in detail.

5. Use `codebook` to find out more about `sexalph`.

6. Use `count` to find out how many hypertensive women there are.

7. Summarize `matage` for hypertensive women.

8. How many hypertensive women have babies with birth weight less than 2000 g?

9. Use `count` to find how many women over 30 are hypertensive.

10. Tabulate the values of `sex`.

11. Make a table of mean birth weight by `sex`.

12. Make a table of median birth weight by `sex`.

13. Generate a new variable called `bwkgs` which is the birth weight in kilograms.

14. Use `display` to calculate $\sqrt{3^2 + 4^2}$.

15. Use `display` to find the probability above 4.3 in a chi-squared distribution on 1 degree of freedom.

Answers to the exercises

Answers to these exercises can be obtained by running the program `chap1` with the command

. chap1

To get the answer for question 8 only, try

. chap1, q(8)

Chapter 2 has no answers, but answers for chapter 3 can be obtained with `chap3` and similarly for the other chapters, up to Chapter 19.

Chapter 2

Tabs, menus and dialog boxes

In Chapter 1 we showed how to do some basic things by typing commands into the command window. There are dialog boxes for helping the user to create these commands, and we shall now demonstrate these by repeating some of the contents of Chapter 1.

2.1   Where to find the dialog boxes

At the top of the Stata window you will see the tabs

File   Edit   Data   Graphics   Statistics   User   Window   Help

Selecting *Data*, *Graphics*, or *Statistics* produces one or more menus and selecting one of the choices in the menus will produce a dialog box which is used for entering information.

2.2   A first look at the data

To load the births data, select the *File* tab (top left hand of screen), then *Open*, and you will see the list of Stata data files in the working directory. Depending on how your version of MS-Windows is set up you will see either `births.dta` or `births` in the list (the extension `.dta` means the file is a Stata data set). Now highlight `births.dta` (or `births`) and select *Open* to load the data. Provided you have copied the files from the CD to `C:\data\hs` the command which is executed to load the data is

```
use "C:\data\hs\births.dta", clear
```

To describe the variables in the births data set select the *Data* tab, then *Describe data*, then *Describe data in memory*. This will bring up a dialog box with various options – ignoring the options and pressing *OK* produces and executes the command:

```
. describe
```

Pressing *Submit* does the same, but leaves the dialog box on the screen. Dialog boxes remember the entries from a previous use, so it may be necessary to press the R button, at the bottom left of the dialog box, to clear any previous selections. Pressing ? (next to R) brings up the help file for the command. Pressing *Cancel* closes the dialog box.

To obtain a summary of the data, select the *Statistics* tab, then *Summaries, tables, and tests*, then *Summary and descriptive statistics*, then *Summary statistics* which calls up a dialog box. Simple summaries of all variable is the default here, so press *Submit* to produce the command

```
. summarize
```

For a more detailed summary of the variable `gestwks` select the option *Display additional statistics* in the *Summary statistics* dialog box, then use the drop down menu for variable names to enter `gestwks` in the *Variables* box. Variable names can also be typed directly in the *Variables* box, and unique abbreviations can be used. Pressing *OK* will produce the command

```
. summarize gestwks, detail
```

You can bring up the dialog box directly by typing

```
. db summarize
```

where `db` stands for dialog box.

To list the values of `matage`, select the *Data* tab, then *Describe data*, then *List data*. Enter `matage` in the *Variables* box, and press *Submit* to produce the command

```
. list matage
```

Click on the *Break* icon to stop the listing. By default a separator line is drawn every five rows, but this can be changed in the *Options* tab in the section called *Table options*. To suppress the listing of observation numbers check the box at the bottom left of the *Main* tab of the dialog box and press *OK* to produce the command:

```
. list matage, noobs
```

Stata commands can be restricted to observations 1, 2, . . . , 5 (for example) by using the *by/if/in* tab in a dialog box. Try

```
. db list
```

to bring up the dialog box, and press the R button, at the bottom left of the dialog box, to clear previous selections. Enter `matage` in the *Variables* box, select the *by/if/in* tab, check *Use a range of observations*, and fill in 1 to 5 (you can type 5 or use the spinner). Press *OK* to produce the command

```
. list matage in 1/5
```

Leaving the *Variables* box blank will list the data for all the variables.

2.3 Tables of frequencies

To obtain the frequencies of the values taken by the categorical variable hyp, select the *Statistics* tab, then *Summaries, tables, and tests*, then *Tables*, then *One-way tables*. Enter hyp in the *Categorical variable* box, and press *OK* to produce the command

```
. tabulate hyp
```

To obtain the two-way frequency table of hyp and sex, select the *Statistics* tab, then *Summaries, tables, and tests*, then *Tables*, then *Two-way tables with measures of association*. Enter hyp in the *Row variable* box and sex in the *Column variable* box, and press *Submit* to produce the command

```
. tabulate hyp sex
```

The basic output from a cross-tabulation reports frequencies only; to include relative frequencies for rows or columns check the option *Within–row relative frequencies*, or the option *Within–column relative frequencies*, in the *Main* tab of the dialog box. These options produce the commands

```
. tabulate hyp sex, row
. tabulate hyp sex, column
```

2.4 Tables of means and other things

To make a table showing the mean and standard deviation of bweight by sex, together with frequencies, select the *Statistics* tab, then *Summaries, tables, and tests*, then *Tables*, then *Table of summary statistics (table)*. Enter sex as the row variable. Then select *Count nonmissing* for the first statistic and enter bweight for the corresponding variable. Select *Mean* for the second statistic and enter bweight for the corresponding variable. Select *Standard deviation* for the third statistic and enter bweight for the corresponding variable. Press *Submit* to produce the command

```
. table sex, contents(count bweight mean bweight sd bweight)
```

The frequencies refer to the number of nonmissing values for bweight in each category of sex.

To make a table of the median and the lower and upper quartiles for birth weight, by sex, press the R button to clear the previous selections. Then enter sex as the *Row variable*. Select *Count nonmissing* for the first statistic and enter beweight for the corresponding variable. Select *Median* for the second statistic and enter bweight for the corresponding variable. Select *Percentile* for the third statistic, use the spinner to select 25, and enter bweight for the corresponding variable. Select *Percentile* for the fourth statistic, use the spinner to select 75, and enter bweight for the corresponding variable. Press *OK* to produce the command

```
. table sex, contents(count bweight median bweight p25 bweight p75 bweight)
```

To make a two-way table showing the mean birth weight by sex and hyp, start with

```
. db table
```

and press R to clear the previous selections. Then enter sex as the *Row variable*, check the *Column variable* box, and hyp as the *Column variable*. Select *Count* as the first statistic with bweight as the corresponding variable. Select *Mean* as the second statistic with bweight as the corresponding variable. Press *OK* to produce the command

```
. table sex hyp, contents(count bweight mean bweight)
```

Another way of making a table showing the mean and standard deviation of several metric variables, such as bweight, gestwks and matage, separately by sex is to select the *Statistics tab*, then *Summaries, tables, and tests*, then *Tables*, then *Table of summary statistics (tabstat)*. Enter bweight, gestwks and matage in the Variables box. Check *Group statistics by variable* and enter sex in the accompanying box. Under *Statistics to display* tick the first box and select *Mean*, then tick the second box and select *Standard deviation*. Press *OK* to produce the command (all one line on the screen)

```
. tabstat bweight gestwks matage, statistics(mean sd)
        by(sex) columns(variables)
```

The option columns(variables) is the default and can be omitted.

2.5   Restricting the scope of commands

To list the id and bweight for those observations for which the logical condition 'birth weight less than 2000 g' is true, start with

```
. db list
```

to bring up the dialog box. Then press R, enter id and bweight in the *Variables* box, and select the *by/if/in* tab, enter bweight < 2000 in the *if* box, and press *OK* to produce the command

```
. list id bweight if bweight < 2000
```

2.6   Generating new variables

To generate a new variable called num1 which takes the value 1 for all observations, select the *Data tab*, then *Create or change variable*, then *Create new variable*. Enter num1 in the *Variable name* box, and 1 in the *Specify a value or an expression* box. Select *byte* in the *Variable type* menu, and press *OK* to produce

19

```
. generate byte num1 = 1
```

The keyword `byte` refers to how the variable will be stored (see Chapter 3). To generate a new variable, `logbw`, which is the natural logarithm of birth weight, try

```
. db generate
```

to bring up the dialog box. Then press R, enter `logbw` in the *Variable name* box, select *Create*, scroll down the list of mathematical functions, double click ln() and enter `bweight` as the argument of ln(). Press *OK* twice to produce

```
. generate logbw = ln(bweight)
```

To change the values of `num1` to 7 (for example), select the *Data* tab, then *Create or change data*, then *Change contents of variable*. Enter `num1` in the *Variable* box, and 7 in the *Contents* box. Press *OK* to produce

```
. replace num1 = 7
```

2.7   Ordering, dropping and keeping

The command

```
. describe
```

shows the list of variables in their current order. To change this order so that `id` and `sex` come first, select the *Data* tab, then *Data utilities*, then *Change the order of variables*. Enter `id` and `sex` in the box labelled *Variables to re-order*, and press *OK* to produce

```
. order id sex, first
```

The option `first` states that `id` and `sex` should be moved to the beginning of the dataset; it is the default and can be omitted. To drop the variables `logbw` and `num1`, select the *Data* tab, then *Variables Manager*. Highlight the variables you wish to drop, right click and select *Drop Selected Variables*. Answer *Yes* to the confirmation to produce

```
. drop num1 logbw
```

To drop observations which satisfy some logical condition (or range) select the *Data* tab, then *Create or change data*, then *Keep or drop observations* and fill in the condition in the *If* box.

2.8 Sorting data

To sort the data according to the value of `matage` (lowest first), select the *Data* tab, then *Sort*, then *Ascending sort*. Enter `matage` in the *Variables* box, and press *Submit* to produce

```
. sort matage
```

The box labelled *Perform stable sort* ensures that tied observations are left in the original order within any ties. To sort on `id` within `matage` enter the variables `matage` and `id` in the *Variables* box, in that order.

2.9 Using Stata as a calculator

To calculate $2 + 3$, select the *Data* tab, then *Other utilities*, then *Hand calculator*. Press *Create*, use the arithmetic keypad to build the expression $2 + 3$, and press *OK*. Press *OK* (again) to produce

```
. display 2 + 3
```

To build the expression $\ln(10)$ try

```
. db display
```

to bring up the dialog box, and press R. Then press *Create*, click on *Functions* and *Mathematical*, scroll down the list of mathematical functions, double click ln() to put $\ln(x)$ in the box at the top, use the keypad to replace x by 10, and press *OK*. Press *OK* (again) to produce

```
. display ln(10)
```

Standard probability functions are readily available. For example, to obtain the probability below 1.96 in a standard normal (i.e. Gaussian) distribution, try

```
. db display
```

to bring up the dialog box and press R. Then select *Create*, click on *Functions* and then on *Probability* and *Density*, scroll down for normal(), double click normal(), use the keypad to build the expression normal(1.96), and press *OK*. Press *OK* (again) to produce

```
. display normal(1.96)
```

Similarly the probability below 3.84 in a chi-squared distribution on 1 degree of freedom, is found by selecting chi2() and building the expression chi2(1 , 3.84).

As a result of repeating some of Chapter 1 using the menus and dialog boxes, you will have seen (we hope) that typing commands is simpler and quicker than using menus and dialog boxes. Menus can be useful when you don't know the name of the command to carry out your requirements, and dialog boxes can be helpful when selecting options, particularly for complex commands.

Exercises

Try some of the exercises in Chapter 1 using menus and dialog boxes rather than commands. There are no solutions for this chapter.

Chapter 3

Housekeeping

Housekeeping refers to all those small jobs which are a nuisance at the time, but make life easier later. This chapter covers how to label and add notes to data; how to label variables and their values; how to recode variables and deal with codes for missing values; how to manage dates; how to save data; and how to use log and do files.

3.1   Labelling a data set

A label can be attached to a data set to remind you what the data refer to, and when the data set was formed. The births data set has already been labelled. After

```
. use births, clear
```

you will see the label 'Data from 500 births' within parentheses. To change this label (or create one) try

```
. label data "Whatever you like"
. describe
```

The label appears in the output of **describe** below the file name and above the date and time when it was last saved. Note that when the label includes spaces, you must enclose it in quotes " ". This can also be done with the dialog box

```
. db label data
```

but note that the quotes are now inserted automatically, so don't put them in yourself.

3.2   Notes

You can also add notes to record the history of the data set so that there no longer needs to be a person who remembers how it came about. For example

```
. notes: This data set was created by George.
```

The text in this command does not require quotes. A time stamp (TS) can also be inserted with

```
. notes: TS This data set was created by George.
```

and the notes for the data set can be displayed with

```
. notes _dta
```

Notes can be specific to variables, and this can be a useful way of reminding yourself how variables are coded. Several such notes have been attached to the births data set, and are displayed in the *Properties* window. Make sure this window is unlocked and then highlight a variable and click on ... in the notes box (the last one of six boxes). Alternatively you can use

```
. notes
```

to show all the notes, or

```
. notes hyp
```

to show only the notes for hyp. To attach a note to a variable, try

```
. notes matage: maternal age in years
```

or use the *Properties* window.

3.3   Labelling variables and their values

After

```
. describe
```

you will see the variable names on the left and their labels on the right. A variable label is used to record further information about the variable. Now try

```
. label var gestwks "Gestation in weeks"
. describe
```

The new label for gestwks has replaced the old one. To remove a label simply label the variable with nothing, as in

```
. label var gestwks
. describe
```

Any notes or labels you create will be lost when you clear the data from memory; to make them a permanent part of the data set you will need to save the new version of the data (see Section 3.8).

The values which a categorical variable takes can also be labelled. By default the labels appear instead of the values in the output of commands such as `tabulate`, but the values can be shown instead of labels with the option `nolabel`. Labelling variable values involves setting up a named mapping between the values and their labels. For example, to label the values of `hyp` using the mapping `hypmap` in which $1 \to$ hyper, $0 \to$ normal, try

```
. label define hypmap 1  "hyper"  0  "normal"
. label values hyp hypmap
```

To check the labels use one of

```
. label list hypmap
. labelbook
```

The frequency table of `hyp` will now show the label for each of its values

```
. tabulate hyp
```

To see the results of `tabulate` without the labels, or to browse the numerical values of this variable without the labels, use the option `nolabel`:

```
. tabulate hyp, nolabel
. browse hyp, nolabel
```

The same label mapping can be used for several variables; for example several Yes/No variables coded 1/2 might have these values labelled as Yes/No. To stop using `hypmap` to label the values of `hyp`, try

```
. label values hyp
. tabulate hyp
```

which labels the values of `hyp` with nothing. To drop `hypmap` altogether, try

```
. label drop hypmap
```

With some care these labelling operations can also be carried out using the *Properties* window.

3.4   Data types and display formats

There are five data types in Stata: byte, integer, long integer, float, and double. What distinguishes them is how much memory they take to store. Variables of type byte take a single byte; integer variables take 2 bytes; long integers take 4 bytes, floating point variables take 4 bytes, and double precision variables take 8 bytes. If you try

```
. describe
```

you will see that **bweight** is stored as type float, while **lowbw** is stored as type byte. These different types need not affect the user - their main function is to economize on memory.

Next to the type, in the results of **describe**, you will see the display format. The default display is a number of width 8, 9, or 10 digits, depending on type. This default works perfectly well without further thought from the user, but it can sometimes be useful to change it, using the **format** command. For example, when listing variables in columns, you may wish to format them to take less room. The Stata symbol for format is % and **%5.2f** means that numeric variable values should be displayed in the form **xx.xx** (i.e. with total width 5, 2 of which are after the decimal point). For string variables f is replaced by s, and the format **%10s** means that 10 is the maximum length of the string, while **%-10s** will left-justify the string. Try

```
. list gestwks in 1/5
. format %4.1f gestwks
. list gestwks in 1/5
```

and see the difference.

3.5 Recoding a variable

Variables can be recoded using **recode**. For example, to create a new variable **sex2** which is the same as **sex** but coded 1 for male and 0 for female, try

```
. recode sex 2=0, generate(sex2)
```

You can check the recoding with

```
. tabulate sex2 sex
```

Of course we could have recoded the variable **sex** directly, but it is generally better to create a new variable rather than to change the original one.

3.6 Missing values

The most commonly used symbol for missing numeric values in Stata is an isolated decimal point, but there are 26 additional symbols, namely

$$.a \quad .b \quad .c \quad \cdots \quad .z$$

which can be useful when it is necessary to distinguish between reasons why the values are missing. When making comparisons or sorting, the following rules are observed:

- all numbers are less than .

- . is less than .a

- .a is less than .b

- .b is less than .c , and so on up to .z

In the births data there are 10 missing values for the variable gestwks. With most commands Stata automatically excludes observations with missing values in any of the variables mentioned in the command. For example

```
. summarize gestwks
```

shows a summary based on the 490 observations with non-missing data. Particular care is needed when using > with missing values, because all missing values are larger than any number. For example, gestwks is missing for 10 subjects, but

```
. count if gestwks > 15
```

returns 500, not 490, because . is > 15. To avoid including the missing observations in this count you need to exclude them yourself with

```
. count if gestwks > 15 & !missing(gestwks)
```

In some data missing values are identified by a code like 9 or −1. To make sure Stata recognizes such values as missing you should change them into a missing value symbol with mvdecode. The data file births_miss.dta has the missing values coded as −1. Load these data with

```
. use births_miss,clear
. summarize
```

and change all occurrences of −1 into the missing code .a with

```
. mvdecode _all, mv(-1=.a)
. summarize
```

3.7   Dates

Dates are tricky to deal with because they are usually coded as string variables, but in order to be able to compare dates, or to calculate elapsed time, it is necessary to convert them into time since some fixed date. The function mdy() returns the number of days since 1/1/1960, so

```
. display mdy(1,1,1960)
```

returns 0, and

```
. display mdy(1,31,1960)
```

27

returns 30. The first number between the brackets indicates the month, the second the day and the last the year (respectively the m, the d and the y of mdy). Check how many days there are between 4 Sep 2000 and 1 Jan 1960. Make sure you don't leave a space between mdy and ( ) and make sure that you enter 4 Sep 2000 as (9,4,2000) not (4,9,2000). The answer is 14,857 days.

The function date() does the same thing for dates which are held as string variables. Several formats are allowed. For example

```
. display date("31/jan/1960", "DMY")
. display date("31/1/1960", "DMY")
. display date("31-jan-1960", "DMY")
. display date("31jan1960", "DMY")
. display date("31011960", "DMY")
```

all give the same results. The second argument in the date function is used to state the order in which the days, months and years appear. Try

```
. display date("jan/31/1960", "MDY")
```

For a full list of available date functions, try

```
. help dates
```

In practice most data hold dates in the form dd/mm/yyyy (Europe) or mm/dd/yyyy (USA). A simple example is shown in the file **dates**. Load these data in memory and describe them with

```
. use dates, clear
. describe
. codebook start
```

You will see that **start** is a string variable which records dates in the European form (dd/mm/yyyy). To generate a new variable **datein** with dates in Stata form, try

```
. generate datein = date(start, "DMY")
. list start datein
```

Note that the new variable **datein** contains days since 1/1/1960, and is numeric. To get the best of both worlds (alphabetic and numeric) we can format the numeric variable **datein** so that it is displayed as a date, using

```
. format datein %td
. list start datein
```

See the *Stata User's Guide (Working with dates and times)* and the Stata FAQs (Frequently Asked Questions) to find out how to deal with dates in which the century has been omitted, such as 21/9/76.

3.8   Saving files

It is sometimes necessary to save the data in memory, for example when labels and notes have been added. This is done with the command `save` which creates a new file on disk, in Stata format, containing the data which are currently in memory. By default, the new file is given the extension `.dta`, and it is saved in your working directory. To over-write a file which already exists in this directory requires the option `replace`. Load the births data and save them in a new file called `mybirths` with the command

```
. use births, clear
. save mybirths
```

Now repeat the command

```
. save mybirths
```

and Stata will refuse to do it, but

```
. save mybirths, replace
```

will work. You should be warned that although data saved under Stata 12 can be loaded in Stata 11, they cannot be loaded in earlier versions. Use `saveold` if you want later to load the file under Stata 9/10. Data saved under any of Stata 9/10/11 can still be loaded in Stata 12.

3.9   Log files

To keep a record of your work while using Stata you can open a log file by clicking on the *Log Begin/Close/Suspend/Resume* icon at the top of the screen. Log files record both commands and output. If the log file is a new one you will be asked to name it: choose, for example, the name `house`. By default the log file will be saved in your working directory with the name `house.smcl`. The extension `.smcl` stands for Stata markup and control language.

If you choose a file name which already exists in your working directory, Stata will ask whether to append the new results to the existing file or to overwrite it. Once the log is open, run a few commands such as

```
. use births, clear
. describe
. summarize
. tabulate hyp
```

To look at the log file you can click on the *Log* icon again and select *View snapshot*. You can copy and paste from this window into your favourite word processing program (see chap 20), or print it as it stands. To close a log file click on the *Log* icon and select *Close* log file.

3.10 Do files

A do file, or batch file, is a text file which contains a list of Stata commands. Its name should have the extension `.do`. It can be created by clicking on the *New Do-file Editor* icon at the top of the screen. Once you are in the *Do-file Editor* enter the commands

```
use births, clear
describe
summarize
tabulate hyp
```

You can execute all or some of these commands using the *Tools* tab at the top of the *Do File Editor*, or you can save the do file in your working directory with the name `myhouse.do` using the Editor's *File* menu. Then, in the command window, you can execute it with the command

```
. do myhouse
```

If Stata does not find your do file you have probably saved it in a directory which is not your working directory - go back to the *Do-file Editor* and check this. If Stata does find your do file it will obey the commands in the file.

A sensible way of working is to open a do file at the start of a session, and to add commands to it as you go along. Each time you run the do file Stata will obey all the commands in it. Comments can be included in the file in several ways:

- begin the line with *

- begin the comment with // (but leave at least one blank before //)

- place the comment within /* and */ delimiters

Examples are given in the *User's Guide* 16.1.2. If you want to leave out one of the commands in your do file, convert it into a comment by inserting * at the beginning. Once you are satisfied that your set of commands is complete, you can open a log file and run the do file one last time to keep a log of the output.

There is another advantage of using do files: they can be re-run whenever you wish and provide a record of what you have done. Because of this it is not necessary to create different versions of the data as new variables are generated and recoded. Instead the generating and recoding can be organized in do files which are run before the analysis starts, and the original data file is left unchanged.

Exercises

1. Open a log file. Load the births data and describe the variables. Replace the current label for the variable `hyp` with the new label "Maternal hypertension", and use `describe` to check that your labelling has worked.

2. Use the command `label define` to create a label mapping called `preterm` which maps the 0 to "normal" and 1 to "pre-term". Use `label list` to check that you have done this correctly.

3. Use the value label `preterm` to label the values of the variable `preterm`. Check the results by tabulating `preterm` with and without the option `nolabel`.

4. Use a file name of your own choosing and create a do file with the *Do-file Editor*. Include in this do file the commands to load the births data, label the values of the variables `preterm` and tabulate `preterm`. Run the do file, and use `browse` to check that the do file has done what you wanted it to do.

5. Use the `date()` function to calculate the number of days which have elapsed between 1/jan/1960 and 4/sep/2000. Do the same for 2000/sep/4.

6. Load the data in the file `dates.dta` and use the `date` function to create two new numerical variables `datein` and `dateout` from the string variables `start` and `stop`. List all the variables. Use the `format` command to format the new variables as dates, and list all the variables again.

7. Calculate the number of days between `datein` and `dateout` for each of the 6 subjects by creating a new variable `days`. List its values and then generate the equivalent number of years by dividing `days` by 365.25.

8. Inspect the contents of the log file by clicking on the Log icon, and checking *View snapshot*. To close the log file, click the Log icon again and check *Close log file*.

Chapter 4

Data input and output

This chapter covers how to load data from text files which have been created by spreadsheets, word processors or text editors; how to load data directly from the keyboard; and how to save data in memory as text files.

4.1 Data sources

Data sets which are stored in Stata format are binary files with extension `.dta`. For example, the births data are in the Stata file `births.dta` which can be loaded into memory with the command `use births`. The command `type` can be used to type out the contents of a file without loading it into memory. Try

`. type births.dta`

and you will see gobbledygook – this is because Stata data files are binary.

To get data into Stata format it is necessary to start from a file of some sort, load this into memory, and then save it as a Stata file with the command `save`. Stata is capable of loading data which have been stored in almost any form, but we shall concentrate on the three most common forms:

- Excel files.

- Text files in which the values of the variables are separated by the tab or comma symbol; these are commonly obtained from database programs such as Access.

- Text files in which the values of the variables are separated by the space symbol; these are commonly obtained from word processors or from a text editor.

To illustrate the methods we have prepared files containing the births data in several ways: `births.xls` is an Excel spreadsheet; `births.tab` is a text file which is tab-separated; `births.dct` is a text file which is space-separated. The reason for the extension `.dct` will become clear in a moment. To look at the contents of `births.tab` try

. `type births.tab`

The first line contains the names of the variables, and the following lines contain their values. Click on the *Break* icon to stop scrolling. To check that the values really are separated by the tab symbol, try

. `type births.tab, showtabs`

To look at the contents of `births.dct` try

. `type births.dct`

and to make sure that the values are *not* separated by tabs, try

. `type births.dct, showtabs`

Note that in this file the variable names are placed in a dictionary (i.e. between curly brackets and preceded by the word `dictionary`), which is why the file has the extension `.dct`. This will be discussed further in Section 4.5.

4.2   Data from an Excel spreadsheet

When the original data are held in an Excel spreadsheet we can import them directly with the command `import excel`. For example to import the data held in `birth.xls` type

. `import excel births.xls,clear firstrow`
. `describe`

The option `firstrow` informs Stata that the first row of the data holds the variable names. If the file holds multiple sheets they can be listed before importing. Try

. `import excel births.xls,describe`
. `import excel births.xls,clear firstrow sheet("Sheet1")`

Excel files with extension `.xls` and `.xlsx` can both be imported.

4.3   Data from a database

When the original data are kept in a table within a database, such as Microsoft Access, the first step – before trying to read them into Stata – is to save them as a text file in which the values of the variables are separated by a tab (or comma) symbol. There are three things to watch out for when doing this:

33

1. Make sure that the variable names do not include spaces – you may need to change the spaces into something like underscore before saving the text file, if they do.

2. Make sure that missing values in the database are coded with a blank (*not* a space).

3. Many database packages will automatically save text files with the extension `.txt`. If you want to save a text file with another extension you may need to enclose the file name in quotes.

One version of the births data was stored in the Access database called `birthsdb.accdb`. To create a Stata file from this you could open `births.accdb` within Access and save the data held in the table as a tab-separated text file with the name `"birthsdb.tab"` (do this by selecting *Export text file* in the *External data* tab and ticking the option *Include Field Names on First Row*). The file `birthsdb.tab` is then loaded in Stata with the command `insheet`, as follows:

```
. insheet using birthsdb.tab, clear
. describe
```

At this stage you would normally save the data in memory so that in future it can be loaded as a Stata data file.

String variables cause no problem with tab- or comma-separated files. The command `insheet` will recognize when a variable takes strings as values, and act accordingly. Sometimes, however, when spaces are entered in the cell of a database which should have been left blank, `insheet` may treat the corresponding variable as a string variable even though all the other values are numerical.

4.4   Data from a word processor

When the original data are kept in a word processor, the first step is to save them as a text file in which the values of the variables are separated by a space symbol. Again there are three things to watch out for:

1. Make sure that the variable names do not include blanks.

2. Make sure that missing values are coded using a Stata missing value symbol.

3. Edit the file and enclose the variable names inside a dictionary, as with `births.dct`.

The command `infile` is used to load the data from `births.dct`, as in

```
. infile using births.dct, clear
. describe
```

Data on string variables can also be loaded with `infile` but each of them must be defined as such in the dictionary. This is done by writing `str#` in front of the variable name, where # is the maximum length of the string for that variable. Try

```
. type births.dct
```

to see how the string variable `sexalph` is defined.

4.5 Large data sets

Stata stores the whole of a data set in memory, so the size of the data set is limited by the size of the memory on your machine. Fortunately most computers these days are equipped with at least 1GB of memory, so this is rarely a problem. Unlike previous versions, Stata 12 manages memory allocation automatically according to the machine you use.

The `insheet` command will automatically choose the data type for the variables so that the data set fits into the smallest possible amount of memory. To achieve the same with `infile` you need first to load the data, and then compress them. Try

```
. infile using births.dct, clear
. describe
```

and you will see that all the numeric variables have been stored as float. Now try

```
. compress
```

and you will see that `bweight`, for example, has been squeezed into an integer, which takes 2 bytes, although originally it was stored as a float, which takes 4 bytes. Alternatively you can include information about how the variables are to be stored, and also how to label them, in the dictionary. Consider, for example, the dictionary file called `births2.dct`, which you can look at with

```
. type births2.dct
```

This contains instructions about the labels to be used for the variables and the type of storage required. When you load it with the command,

```
. infile using births2.dct, clear
. describe
```

you will see that the variables have been labelled and also that they have been stored as integer, float, byte, or string, depending on the storage type used in the dictionary.

If you are faced with a file format which is outside the range of the methods described here, the *Stata User's Guide (Inputting and importing data)* has an excellent step-by-step account of how to load data into memory, which covers all the possibilities.

Table 4.1: Mortality rates per 100 000 by employment grade and categories of age

grade	agecat	rate
1	40	4.9
1	45	6.1
1	50	13.2
2	40	6.4
2	45	8.8
2	50	16.2

4.6   Loading data from the keyboard

Only in rare cases would one load data directly into Stata from the keyboard, but it can be useful for very small data sets. It is best to do this with the *Data Editor*, after clearing any data from memory with `clear`.

Start by clicking on the *Data Editor (Edit)* icon. To load the values of the 3 variables `grade`, `agecat` and `rate`, shown in Table 4.1, type their values in the spreadsheet that appears when the *Data Editor* is called. Don't type in the names of the variables as the first row - just type the values, row by row. After typing each value in a row before the last, press the *Tab* key, but after the last value in a row press the *Enter* key and use the cursor to return to the beginning of the next row. When you have completed the data entry, close the *Data Editor* and check your editing by listing the data in memory. Any mistakes can be corrected by recalling the *Data Editor*. Stata automatically names each column (i.e. each variable) as `var1`, `var2`, etc. To change `var1` into `grade` open the *Data Editor* again, highlight `var1` in the *Variables* window, and use the *Properties* window to change `var1` into `grade`. Press *Enter* after changing the name of each variable.

The commands

```
. clear
. input grade agecat rate
```

can be used instead of the *Data Editor*. After typing in the data for the first row, separated by spaces, press *Enter* and continue with the second row. After the last row type `end`. The data in Table 4.1 will now be in memory.

4.7   Data output

To save the data in memory as an Excel try

```
. export excel using grade.xls, firstrow(var)
```

36

where `firstrow(var)` saves the variable names in the first row. To save these data as a text file called `grade.raw`, without variable names, try

```
. outfile using grade.raw, replace
. type grade.raw
```

To include a dictionary, type

```
. outfile using grade.dct, dictionary
. type grade.dct
```

The command `outfile` is the output equivalent of `infile`. The output equivalent of `insheet` is `outsheet`, and can be used to output text files with tab separators. For example, try

```
. outsheet using grade.tab
. type grade.tab, showtabs
```

The commands `save`, `outsheet` and `outfile` all allow the option `replace`. To save as a SAS XPORT file use `export sasxport` in place of `save`. Similarly to load a SAS XPORT file use `import sasxport` in place of `use`.

Exercises

1. Load the data in `example.dta` and have a look at the values of the variables.

2. These data are also in the tab-separated file `example.tab`. Use `type` to inspect this file, then load it into memory using `insheet`.

3. The same data are also in the dictionary file `example.dct` which has space-separated values. Use `type` to inspect this file, use `infile` to load the data into memory, and check that the data which have been loaded are the same as the data in the file.

4. Clear the memory and use the Data editor to load the data shown below

id	time	grp	sex
6	21.7	2	f
7	6.2	2	m
8	35.4	1	m
9	20.0	1	f
10	9.3	2	m

   Close the Data editor, and list the data in memory.

Chapter 5

Graph commands

The Stata graph commands allow easy access to high-quality graphs plus the ability to over-ride the defaults and to arrange the layout in virtually any way you want. In this chapter we show how to produce basic graphics such as box plots, histograms, scatter plots, and line plots, using commands. When producing complicated graphs it is best to use the *Graph* dialogs because these take care of remembering the endless option names. *Graph* dialogs will be described in the next chapter.

5.1   Box plots

To make a box plot of birth weight using the births data, try

```
. use births, clear
. graph box bweight
```

After a few seconds you will see a box plot where the box indicates the median and the two quartiles. The vertical lines above and below the box indicate the range of values, with outliers shown as separate points (see the *Stata Graphics Reference Guide* in the documentation for more details). To make the box thinner, try

```
. graph box bweight, outergap(50)
```

which specifies that the gap between the edge of the graph and the first box should be 50% of the width of the box. The box can be drawn horizontally with

```
. graph hbox bweight, outergap(50)
```

The main use of box plots is when several are placed side by side, as in the comparison of the distribution of birth weight for babies of normal and hypertensive mothers, stratified by sex:

```
. graph box bweight, outergap(50) over(hyp)
. graph box bweight, outergap(50) over(hyp) over(sexalph)
```

The command

```
. graph box bweight, outergap(50) over(hyp) by(sexalph)
```

does almost the same thing, but `by( )` makes two separate subgraphs within the graph, while `over( )` puts all results on one plot.

5.2   Histograms

To make a histogram of birth weight, try

```
. histogram bweight
```

The rectangles in the histogram are called bins by Stata, and the height of each bin is the relative frequency per unit of birth weight (i.e. per gram). The appearance of the graph is not too bad, but you might wish to change where the first bin starts, how wide the bins are, and the vertical axis from density to percent, with

```
. histogram bweight, percent start(0) width(500)
```

There is no `over` option with `histogram` but `by` can be used. For example

```
. histogram bweight, percent start(0) width(500) by(sexalph)
. histogram bweight, percent start(0) width(500) by(sexalph hyp)
```

To superimpose a normal curve on the histogram, try

```
. histogram bweight, percent start(0) width(500) normal
```

The superimposed normal curve has the same mean and standard deviation as the variable `bweight`.

Although there is a `discrete` option for `histogram`, histograms of categorical variables are best produced as bar charts. To make a bar chart of the percentage frequencies of the values of `hyp`, create new variables called `hyp0` and `hyp1` with

```
. separate hyp, by(hyp)
```

then try

```
. graph bar (count) hyp0 (count) hyp1, percentages
```

Ways of improving the look of bar charts will be described in the next chapter.

Command	What it does
`twoway scatter yvar xvar`	Scatter plot
`twoway lfit yvar xvar`	Best fitting line
`twoway line yvar xvar`	Line plot
`twoway connected yvar xvar`	Connected point plot
`twoway rcap lower upper xvar`	Vertical capped lines for confidence intervals

Table 5.1: Commonly used twoway commands

5.3   Scatter plots

Scatter plots can be used to evaluate the association between two metric variables such as `bweight` and `gestwks`. Try

```
. twoway scatter bweight gestwks
```

The plot suggests that there is a roughly linear association between birth weight and gestation period. To change the symbol which marks the points to a small x, try

```
. twoway scatter bweight gestwks, msymbol(smx)
```

For a list of marker symbols and sizes, try

```
. graph query symbolstyle
. graph query markersizestyle
```

To produce separate plots for boys and girls, try

```
. twoway scatter bweight gestwks, msymbol(smx) by(sexalph)
```

The `twoway` command includes many possible plot-types, and some of the more commonly used ones are listed in Table 5.1.

5.4   Overlaying graphs

Plots produced for different subsets of the data, like baby boys and girls, can be overlaid. For example, try

```
. twoway scatter bweight gestwks if sex==1, msymbol(smcircle) mcolor(blue)
```

to produce the scatter plot of `bweight` against `gestwks` for boys, and

```
. twoway scatter bweight gestwks if sex==2, msymbol(smx) mcolor(red)
```

to produce the scatter plot for girls. To overlay these, try

```
. twoway (scatter bweight gestwks if sex==1,
        msymbol(smcircle) mcolor(blue))
        (scatter bweight gestwks if sex==2,
        msymbol(smx) mcolor(red))
```

The legend is not helpful, so add the option

```
, legend(label(1 "Boys") label(2 "Girls"))
```

where the number 1 stands for the first key and 2 for the second. Note that quotes are needed here. Be very careful with the comma as this option applies to the whole graph. The syntax when overlaying two or more twoway plots is

```
. twoway ( ... , options ) ( ... , options) , options
```

where the first `options` refers to the first plot, the second `options` refers to the second plot, and the third to the overall graph.

5.5   Line plots

The data set `meanbw.dta` is derived from the births data set, and holds the mean and standard error of the mean for the birth weights of babies by `agegrp` where `agegrp` contains the mid-point of the interval for maternal age to which the mother belongs, using the intervals (20–30), (30–35), (35–40), and (40–45). Load the data and have a look at them with

```
. use meanbw, clear
. list
```

To plot the mean birth weights against age group as a scatter plot, try

```
. twoway scatter mbw agegrp
```

To connect the points on the scatter plot, try

```
. sort agegrp
. twoway connected mbw agegrp
```

To show only the lines, try

```
. twoway line mbw agegrp
```

The difference between `line` and `connected` is that `line` does not show marker symbols for the points which are joined by lines, while `connected` does.

It is sometimes useful to add error bars to plots of means. Try

```
. generate lower = mbw - 1.96 * sem
. generate upper = mbw + 1.96 * sem
```

to create the upper and lower bounds. To plot these against `agegrp`, joining them with vertical capped lines, try

. `twoway rcap lower upper agegrp`

To overlay this plot with the connected mean values, try

. `twoway (rcap lower upper agegrp)(connected mbw agegrp)`

A quick way of adding error bars to a plot of means is to use the `serrbar` command, which avoids the need to generate variables containing lower and upper confidence limits:

. `serrbar mbw sem agegrp, scale(1.96)`

To connect the means, a further line plot can be added with the option `addplot`:

. `serrbar mbw sem agegrp, scale(1.96) addplot(line mbw agegrp)`

5.6   Cumulative distribution plots

Like box plots, cumulative distribution function (cdf) plots (also called cumulative probability plots) are better than histograms for metric data because they don't require you to choose the number or width of the bins. Stata has no command for producing cumulative distribution plots directly, although a number have been written by users, among them `cdfplot`. This is included with the files which come with the book (see Chapter 0), but if you have an internet connection it can also be installed with

. `ssc install cdfplot, replace`

The advantage of installing it from the SSC site is that this will be the latest version. Now try

. `use births, clear`
. `cdfplot bweight`

This type of plot is useful when comparing several distributions on the same graph. For example,

. `cdfplot bweight, by(hyp)`

shows two cumulative distributions, one for normal mothers, one for hypertensive mothers. Note the staircase effect when `cdfplot` is used with a variable such as `matage` which takes only a limited number of values:

. `cdfplot matage`

To produce a cumulative distribution plot of `matage` using only Stata commands it is necessary first to calculate the cumulative relative frequencies with the command `cumul`, and then to place them in a variable called (for example) `cdf`:

```
. cumul matage, generate(cdf) equal
```

The option `equal` forces observations that share the same value of `matage` to have the same cumulative relative frequency. The cumulative relative frequencies are then plotted against the values of `matage` using a line graph:

```
. twoway line cdf matage, connect(stairstep) sort
```

The `connect` option in this example states that the points are to be connected using a stairstep which is a horizontal line followed by a vertical line. Try `graph query connectstyle` for a full list of connect options.

5.7   Adding lines

Vertical lines can be added through any point on the X-axis with `xline( )`. Similarly horizontal lines can be added with `yline( )`. These options can be repeated to add several lines. As an example, try

```
. twoway scatter bweight gestwks, xline(39) yline(2500 3000) yline(3500)
```

It is often useful, with a scatter plot, to overlay the best fitting straight line. For example, try

```
. twoway scatter bweight gestwks
```

to produce the scatter plot of birth weight versus gestation period, and

```
. twoway lfit bweight gestwks
```

to plot the best fitting straight line. To overlay the two graphs, try

```
. twoway (lfit bweight gestwks) (scatter bweight gestwks)
```

and to see the confidence interval about the fitted line, try

```
. twoway (lfitci bweight gestwks) (scatter bweight gestwks)
```

5.8   Graph titles

Stata allows four possible sorts of title for a graph: title, subtitle, caption, and note. To see where they go, and their relative sizes, try

```
. twoway scatter bweight gestwks,
        title(TITLE) subtitle(SUBTITLE) caption(CAPTION) note(NOTE)
```

When a graph command is combined with **by**, the graph is repeated for each category of the variable in the **by**. Try

```
. twoway scatter bweight gestwks,
        title(TITLE) subtitle(SUBTITLE) caption(CAPTION) note(NOTE)
        by(sexalph)
```

and you will see two graphs with identical titles. When the subtitle is not set that position is used to identify the graphs using the values of **sexalph**. Try

```
. twoway scatter bweight gestwks, by(sexalph) title(TITLE)
```

and you will see that each graph has the title 'TITLE', and the graphs are identified in the subtitle position using the values of **sexalph**. To make the title refer to the entire graph it must be inside the **by**, as in

```
. twoway scatter bweight gestwks, by(sexalph, title(TITLE))
```

If you want to set your own overall note this must also be within the **by**, as in

```
. twoway scatter bweight gestwks, by(sexalph, title(TITLE) note(MYNOTE))
```

The automatic subtitles and notes can be removed using **subtitle("")** outside the **by( )** and **note("")** inside the **by( )**.

When the variable in the **by( )** is numeric, the values it takes are used to identify the graphs. For example, try

```
. twoway scatter bweight gestwks, by(sex)
```

To replace the numeric codes with text first label the values of **sex**:

```
. label define sex 1 "Boys" 2 "Girls"
. label values sex sex
. twoway scatter bweight gestwks, by(sex)
```

Check that the graphs are now identified as Boys and Girls. For convenience a number of generally applicable options like **title** are gathered together in Table 5.2.

5.9   Titles and labels for axes

Axis titles are the words appearing alongside an axis and axis labels are the numbers which appear by the tick marks. The default title for an axis is the variable label, or failing this, the name of the variable plotted on that axis. After

```
. describe
. twoway scatter bweight gestwks
```

you will see that the X-axis has the title 'gestation period', which is the label for the variable `gestwks`, while the Y-axis has the title 'birth weight'. To change the size of the default title for the X-axis, try

```
. twoway scatter bweight gestwks, xtitle(, size(large))
```

and to change the default title as well, try

```
. twoway scatter bweight gestwks,
        xtitle(Gestation period in weeks, size(large))
```

Quotes are not required for titles. Special characters can be included using the *smcl* notation. For example θ is inserted in a title as `{&theta}`, while Θ is inserted as `{&Theta}`. The word George in bold font is indicated by `{bf:George}` while the same thing in italics is `{it:George}`. Some mathematical symbols can also be included. For a full list of available characters see `help graph_text`.

The default labels for an axis are the best round numbers that cover the range of values taken by the variable. To change the default for the Y-axis, try

```
. twoway scatter bweight gestwks, ylabel(1000(500)5000)
```

The expression 1000(500)5000 is short for 1000, 1500, 2000, ... , 5000 and is an example of a number list. You can change the size of the labels and the angle with

```
. twoway scatter bweight gestwks,
        ylabel(1000(500)5000, labsize(large) angle(horizontal))
```

Some of the more common general options for graphs are shown in Table 5.2.

5.10   Naming, saving, and combining graphs

Graphs can be saved either in memory or on disk. The graph window can be minimised and recalled, but when you create a new graph it will over-write the first one. To keep the graph more permanently you need to name it. For example,

```
. twoway scatter bweight gestwks, name(mygraph)
```

will name the scatter plot `mygraph` and the graph can be displayed at any time with

```
. graph display mygraph
```

To replace a graph with a new one bearing the same name, try

```
. twoway scatter bweight matage, name(mygraph, replace)
```

The graph `mygraph` is saved in memory, and lost when the session is closed, but graphs can also be saved (with a name) to disk. For example

Group	Option
Graph titles	`title(text, size( ))`
	`subtitle(text, size( ))`
	`caption(text, size( ))`
	`note(text, size( ))`
with `by`	place the above options inside the `by( )`
Axes	`xtitle(text, size( ))`
	`ytitle(text, size( ))`
	`xlabel(numlist, labsize( ) angle( ))`
	`ylabel(numlist, labsize( ) angle( ))`
	`xscale(range(numlist) log)`
	`yscale(range(numlist) log)`
Added lines	`xline(#, lpattern( ) lcolor( ))`
	`yline(#, lpattern( ) lcolor( ))`
Marker symbols	`msymbol( ) msize( ) mcolor( ) mlabel( )`
Connect style	`connect( )`
Legends	`legend(label(# "text") label(# "text") ...)`
	`legend(order(# "text" # "text") ...)`

Table 5.2: Some general options for graphs

. `graph save mygraph`

will save the current graph as `mygraph.gph` where `gph` is the default extension for Stata graphs. If a file with that name already exists, add the option `replace`. Any saved graph can be retrieved at a later time with the command `graph use`. For example try

. `graph use mygraph`

Graphs can be dropped from memory with

. `graph drop mygraph`

and erased from disk with

. `erase mygraph.gph`

You can combine different graphs with the command `graph combine` either from memory or from disk. For example

. `twoway scatter bweight matage, name(bw_age)`
. `twoway scatter bweight gestwks, name(bw_gest)`
. `graph combine bw_age bw_gest`

will combine the two named graphs into a single graph showing the two scatter plots side by side. Alternatively, try

```
. twoway scatter bweight matage, saving(bw_age)
. twoway scatter bweight gestwks, saving(bw_gest)
. graph combine bw_age.gph bw_gest.gph
```

which will combine the two graphs from disk. Note that the extension .gph is required when using graph combine with graphs saved on disk. Any number of graphs can be combined.

5.11 Printing and exporting graphs

Whenever a graph is produced it can be printed using the *File* tab and then *Print Graph*, or you can click on the *Print* icon. Graphs can also be copied directly onto the clip-board using the *Edit* tab in the Graph window, and then *Copy Graph*. They can then be pasted into documents created by most word processors.

To export a current graph as a .pdf file, called for example mygraph.pdf, use

```
. twoway scatter bweight gestwks
. graph export mygraph.pdf
```

Note that the graph which is saved is the current graph, and mygraph.pdf refers to the name of the file in which it will be saved. For a full list of the export possibilities, try

```
. help graph_export
```

5.12 Schemes

Schemes govern the default appearance of graphs. The scheme which is set when Stata is first installed is called **s2color**. For a list of available schemes, try

```
. help schemes
```

To see what the economist scheme looks like, try

```
. twoway scatter bweight gestwks, scheme(economist)
```

You can change the scheme permanently to economist with

```
. set scheme economist, perm
```

5.13 Help for graphics

Help may be required on many different aspects of a graph command, and it is not always clear how to get it. When in doubt, start with help graph_intro. A list of some other useful sources of help is given below.

Command	Help for
graph query symbolstyle	List of main plotting symbols
graph query markersizestyle	List of sizes for plotting symbols
graph query colorstyle	List of colors for plotting symbols
graph query linepatternstyle	List of patterns for lines
help title_options	Graph titles
help axis_options	Axes
help added_line_options	Added lines
help marker_options	Marker symbols
help connect_options	Connecting points
help legend_options	Legends

Exercises

1. Load the births data and obtain box plots of gestwks for each category of lowbw. Add a title and improve the labelling of the Y-axis.

2. Plot a histogram for the metric variable gestwks. Label the X-axis from 20 to 45 using intervals of 5. Start the first bin at 20, and use 5 as the bin width.

3. Obtain a scatter plot of gestwks vs matage together with the best fitting line.

Chapter 6

Graph dialog boxes

There is a lot more to Stata graphs than we have shown in the preceding chapter, and most of this is best explored using the graph dialog boxes. Dialog boxes can be called up from the *Graphics* tab or directly with (for example)

```
. db histogram
```

It is not our intention to provide a complete survey of all the graph dialog boxes, only to introduce a few of them so that the general style becomes familiar.

6.1 Histograms

Start by loading the `births` data and doing a bit of house keeping:

```
. use births, clear
. label define sexmap 1 "Male" 2 "Female"
. label value sex sexmap
```

Now call up the dialog box for histograms with

```
. db histogram
```

and press R to remove any previous selections.

The main tab

To make a histogram of the categorical (discrete) variable `matage` enter `matage` in the *Variable* box, check *Data are discrete* and *Percent*, and press *Submit* to produce

```
. histogram matage, discrete percent
```

You can improve this by clicking *Bar properties* in the *Histogram* dialog box to produce a 'child' dialog box. In this select dark green for the fill color and change the bar gap to 10. Pressing *Submit* produces

```
. histogram matage, discrete percent fcolor(dkgreen) gap(10)
```

If you want to make further selections before producing the graph you can press *Accept* in the child dialog box, rather than *Submit*. Note that the *Bar properties* tab now has an asterix to indicate that these properties have been changed.

To make a histogram of the metric (continuous) variable `bweight` call up the dialog box for histograms and press R to remove any previous selections. Select the *Main* tab and enter `bweight` in the *Variable* box. Check *Width of bins* and enter 500, check *Lower limit of first bin* and enter 0, and check *Percent*. Pressing *Submit* will produce

```
. histogram bweight, width(500) start(0) percent
```

Click on *Bar properties* and experiment with the options which refer to the color used for filling and outlining the bins. Return to the defaults when you have finished, but leave the selections for *Width of bins*, *Lower limit of first bin*, and *Percent*.

The Titles tab

Select the *Titles* tab and enter TITLE for the title, SUBTITLE for the subtitle, CAPTION for the caption and NOTE for the note. Press *Submit* to see where these appear. Click on *Properties* for each of these and experiment with different sizes, colors, and positions. Then remove all titles and return to the defaults for this tab when you have finished.

The Overall tab

The controls in this tab are concerned with the overall appearance of the graph and allow you to change the scheme, and to name the graph so that it is stored in memory. Click on *Region properties* to see the options for the graph and plot regions. Select a different fill color for each of the regions, and see what happens. You can also experiment with different colors for the outlines. Return to the default values for this tab when you have finished experimenting.

The By tab

Select the *By* tab and check the *Draw subgraphs for unique values of variables* box. Enter `sex` in the *Variables* box and press *Submit* to produce

```
. histogram bweight, width(500) start(0) percent by(sex)
```

You will get one subgraph for each category of `sex`. Checking *Add a graph with totals* includes a total graph, but cancel this before proceeding to the next section.

The X axis and Y axis tabs

These two tabs contain identical controls. Select the *X axis* tab, enter `Birth weight in gms` for the *Title*. The options in this menu allow you to choose the range the scale must cover, how many ticks, etc. Under *Major tick/label properties* choose custom, enter 0(1000)5000 as the *Custom rule* and press *Accept* and then *Submit* to produce

```
. histogram bweight, width(500) start(0) percent
           xtitle(Birth weight in gms) xlabel(0(1000)5000) by(sex)
```

The if/in, Weights, Density plots tabs

These are straightforward. The *Weights* tab shows which sort of weights are allowed (only frequency weights with histogram) and the *Density plots* gives a choice between adding a normal density plot based on the data mean and standard deviation or one fitted to the histogram using a kernel density estimation (or both).

The Legend tab

Use the *Density plots* tab to add a normal density plot to the histogram of `bweight` and then open the *Legend* tab and check *Show legend*. Press *Submit* to produce

```
. histogram bweight, width(500) start(0) normal xtitle(Birth weight in gms)
           xlabel(0(1000)5000) by(, legend(on)) by(sex)
```

The Add plots tab

This is not particularly useful with histograms.

6.2   Box plots

Start by closing the dialog box for histograms and calling up the one for for box plots with `db box`. Press R to remove any previous selections.

The Main tab

Enter `bweight` in the *Variables* box and press *Submit* to produce

```
. graph box bweight
```

The Boxes tab

You can choose between *Line*, *Custom line* and a *Marker* to indicate the median. Choose *Marker*, set the outside gap in the *Global box setting* of this tab to 150 (i.e. 150%) and press *Submit* to produce a box with gaps 1.5 times its size on each side:

```
. graph box bweight, outergap(150) medtype(marker)
```

The *Boxes tab* can be used to change the fill color for the boxes, but note that when only one variable is specified in the *Main* tab only one fill color can be selected – the others make no difference.

The Categories tab

The *Categories* tab is used to produce several subplots on the same graph. Select the *Categories* tab, and then

- Check *Group 1*, enter `hyp` in the *Grouping variable* box and under *Properties* check the *Override labels for this group*.

- Enter `1 "Normal" 2 "Hyper"` in the *Label specification*. Pressing *Properties* spawns a child dialog box, so press *Accept* to return to the parent.

- Now check *Group 2*, enter `sex` in the *Grouping variable* box and under *Properties* check the *Override labels for this group* and enter `1 "Boys" 2 "Girls"` in the *Label specification*.

- Press *Accept* and then *Submit* to produce

```
. graph box bweight, over(hyp, relabel(1 "Normal" 2 "Hyper"))
     over(sex, relabel(1 "Boys" 2 "Girls")) outergap(150) medtype(marker)
```

and see four box plots corresponding to the four combinations of `hyp` and `sex`.

The By tab

The *By* tab is used to produce several subgraphs on the same graph. As an alternative to putting the box plots for all four combinations of `hyp` and `sex` remove `sex` as the grouping variable for category 2 in the *Categories* tab, select the *By* tab, check *Draw subgraphs for unique values of variables*, enter `sex` in the *Variables* box, and press *Submit* to produce

```
. graph box bweight, over(hyp, relabel(1 "Normal" 2 "Hyper"))
        outergap(150) medtype(marker) by(sex)
```

More than one Y variable

Start by generating two new variables, one for the birth weight of boys and one for that of girls, with

```
. separate bweight, by(sex)
```

Then select the *Main* tab in the *Graph box* dialog box, press R, and enter `bweight1` and `bweight2` in the *Variables* box. Press submit to produce

```
. graph box bweight1 bweight2
```

Note that the two boxplots have been drawn in different colors, automatically. Now select the *Categories* tab and reinstate `hyp` as the first grouping variable. Press properties, check *Override the labels for this group* and enter 1 "Normal" 2 "Hyper" in the *Label specification* box. Press *Accept* and then *Submit* to produce

```
. graph box bweight1 bweight2, over(hyp, relabel(1 "Normal" 2 "Hyper"))
```

The Legends tab

The legend for this last plot is not very good, so select the *Legend* tab, check *Override default keys*, and enter 1 "Boys" 2 "Girls" in the *Specify order of keys and optionally change labels* box. Press *Submit* to produce

```
. graph box bweight1 bweight2, over(hyp, relabel(1 "Normal" 2 "Hyper"))
      legend(order(1 "Girls" 2 "Boys"))
```

The rest of the tabs

These all behave like their equivalents in the histogram dialog box, except for the *Options* tab which is a catch-all for some minor points.

6.3   Bar charts

To make a bar chart showing the mean birth weight for boys and girls, close the dialog box for box plots and bring up the one for bar charts with `db bar`. Select the *Main* tab, check the first box under *Statistics to plot*, and enter `bweight1` in the first *Variable* box. Note that the default statistic to plot is the mean. Check the second box and enter `bweight2` in the second *Variable* box. Press *Submit* to produce

```
. graph bar (mean) bweight1 (mean) bweight2
```

This is a bit chunky, so select the *Bars* tab, and under *Global settings* set the gap between bars to 50 and the outside gap to 150. Press *Submit* to produce

```
. graph bar (mean) bweight1 (mean) bweight2, bargap(50) outergap(150)
```

The labelling can be improved: select the *Legend* tab and override the default keys with 1 "Boys" 2 "Girls". Then select the *Y axis* tab and give it the title `Birth weight in gms`. Press *Submit* to see the improvements. Instead of *mean* you could have selected *median* or any other possibility in the pull down menu under *Statistic* in the *Main* tab.

As it stands it is not a very interesting bar chart, but we could make it more interesting by selecting the *Categories* tab and entering `hyp` for the first grouping variable. Press *Submit* to see the result. The labelling could be improved by clicking on the *Properties* for the first grouping variable, checking the ovveride, and entering `1 "Normal" 2 "Hyper"` in the *Label specification* box. Press *Submit* and close the dialog box when you have finished.

To make a bar chart of the frequencies of a categorical variable such as `hyp` follow the same procedure: first separate the values of `hyp` into new variables `hyp0` and `hyp1` with

```
. separate hyp, by(hyp)
```

then bring up the dialog box for bar charts with `db bar`. Select the *Main* tab, check the first box under *Statistics to plot*, select *Percentage* and enter `hyp0` in the first *Variable* box. Check the second box under *Statistics to plot*, select *Percentage* and enter `hyp1` in the second *Variable* box. Press *OK* to produce

```
. graph bar (count) hyp0 (count) hyp1, percentages
```

The size of the bars, the gap between them, and the legend, can all be improved in the same way as in the previous example, producing something like

```
. graph bar (count) hyp0 (count) hyp1, percentages bargap(50)
          outergap(1 50) blabel(bar, size(medium))
          legend(on order(1 "0" 2 "1"))
```

6.4   Twoway graphs

Start with

```
. db twoway
```

and click on *Create* to create a plot. Select *Scatter* as the type of basic plot, and enter `bweight` as the Y variable and `gestwks` as the X variable. Press *Submit* to produce

```
. twoway (scatter bweight gestwks)
```

The parentheses are not necessary, but do no harm. The *Marker properties* button refers to the symbols used for the points in the plot, and allows you to select the symbol and color for the marker. The *Add labels to markers* group allows you to enter the name of the variable whose values will be used to label the points (e.g. `sex`). The *if/in* tab allows you to restrict the scope of the plot, e.g. by entering `sex==1` in the *if* box.

To add further plots you need to go back to the first dialog box by pressing *Accept* and then *Create* to create a new plot. For example, to add the line of best fit to a scatter plot, create a second plot, check *Fit plots* and enter `bweight` and `gestwks` as the Y and X variables. Press *Submit* to produce

```
. twoway (scatter bweight gestwks) (lfit bweight gestwks)
```

As another example, go back to the *Twoway* dialog box and

- Select Plot 1, check *Edit*, select the *if/in* tab and add `sex==1` to the *if* box.

- Press *Accept*, then *Edit*, and under the *Markers properties* tab in the *Plot* tab select a small circle for symbol, black for color, and press *Accept* twice.

- Now disable Plot 2 and create a third plot using the same X and Y variables, but adding `sex==2` to the *if* box for this plot, and select a large red cross for the marker.

- Press *Accept* and then *Submit* to produce

```
. twoway (scatter bweight gestwks if sex==1, mcolor(black) msymbol(smcircle))
         (scatter bweight gestwks if sex==2, mcolor(red) msymbol(lgx))
```

This time the legend needs improving, so select the *Legend* tab in the first dialog box (you need to press *Accept* to get back to this) and override the default keys with `1 "Boys" 2 "Girls"`.

6.5   The graph editor

If you can't remember the appropriate graph commands, and find the graph menus difficult to navigate, a useful strategy is to start with a simple graph and then to use the graph editor to improve it. Note that although you end up with an improved graph, you will not have a graph command to re-create it, so you must save it or record the edits used to produce it. To demonstrate the use of the graph editor start with

```
. twoway (scatter bweight gestwks) (lfit bweight gestwks)
```

which creates a scatter plot of `bweight` versus `gestwks` together with the line of best fit. Then right click on the graph, select *Start Graph Editor*, and maximise the graph window. In the centre of the screen you will see the graph you want to edit, to the left you will see five icons for the editing tools, and to the right you will see the list of the objects which make up the graph. If the object list takes up too much space you can use the mouse to move the right hand side of the graph window further to the right. Now run the mouse over the 5 icons, and you will see that they are called *Pointer*, *Add Text*, *Add Line*, *Add Marker* and *Grid Edit*. The last of these is an advanced feature so we shall restrict ourselves to the first four. The pointer is selected by default when you open the graph editor; to select any other tool just click on the icon.

The pointer

Using the pointer, click on one of the points in the scatter plot. You will see a red box surrounding the points, and a new (contextual) toolbar at the top of the screen which contains the options you are most likely to use having selected the points in the scatter plot. For example, if you click on the drop down menu for *color*, and select *maroon*, you will see the points change color to maroon. Similarly, clicking on the drop down menu for *symbol* and selecting *small* X changes the symbol for the points to a small X.

Now click on the left axis, and again you will see a red box, this time surrounding the axis, plus a new contextual tool bar at the top of the screen. Click on the drop down menu for *Label angle*, and select *Horizontal* to make the labels on the axis horizontal instead of vertical. To add more ticks click on *Axis rule* and check *Suggest # of ticks*. A dialog box will appear in which you can enter 10. Pressing *OK* shows the axis with 10 ticks (pressing *Apply* leaves the dialog box in place, in case you change your mind).

To add a title the easiest thing to do is click on *title* in the list of objects in the object browser on the right hand side of the graph. The contextual tool bar will now show a box in which you can enter a title such as `Birth Weight versus Gestation`. Press enter to see where Stata has positioned the title, and use the pointer to move it around. Properties of the title can be changed by clicking *More* next to the text box.

Now use the pointer to select the title of the *x axis* (`gestation period`) or alternatively click *title* under *xaxis1* in the object browser. Using the contextual toolbar you can edit the title, increase its size, change its color, etc., and using the pointer you can move it around. Finish editing the title, and use the pointer to select the *x axis*. Using the contextual toolbar you can now add more labels, change the size of the labels, etc.

Add Marker

Click on the *Add Marker tool* and notice that in the contextual toolbar the default marker is a hollow circle, and the default size is large. We shall stick with these defaults. Now identify the most extreme point in the right-hand corner and click on it to mark it with a hollow circle.

Add Text

Select the *Add Text* tool and click somewhere near (but not too near) the point you have marked. A dialog box will appear in which to enter the text, for example `Extreme Point`. Press *OK* and you will see the text starting where you clicked.

Add Line

Select the *Add Line* tool and in the contextual toolbar click on *Arrowhead* and select *Head*. Now use the mouse to draw a line from the text to the marked point by starting at the text and holding the left mouse button down until the line is finished.

As another example of adding lines use the pointer to select the *x axis* and click *More* in the contextual toolbar.

- At the bottom of the dialog box press *Edit or add individual ticks or labels*. Click on *Add* and fill in 37 for the value. Press *OK* and close the window.

- Now click on *Reference line*, and enter 37 for the *X axis value*. Pressing *OK* twice will show a vertical line through 37 weeks of gestation.

- Finally select the *Add Text* tool and click somewhere to the left of the line through 37 weeks. Enter word `Preterm` in the dialog box and press *OK*.

You can move the text around as before by using the *Pointer tool*.

6.5.1 Recording the edits

At any time after the *Graph Editor* has started you can record your edits by clicking on the red button in the top row of icons. Clicking again will stop the recording and bring up a dialog box asking whether you want to save the recording. You may choose any name. Once saved the recording can be applied to any graphs, although the edits may not always make sense. Help on recording can be obtained with `help graph_editor`.

Undoing edits

There are several ways to undo changes made with the graph editor. To undo an edit immediately after you have done it you can use the *Undo* icon (at the top of the graph editor window) or you can use the pointer to right-click on the edit and select delete. For example, select the *Add Marker* tool and mark an arbitrary point. Now select the pointer, right click on the point, and select delete - the marker will disappear (but not the point). It is not possible to delete or move parts of the original graph, but you can hide them (the option appears when you right-click on the item). If you have done several edits, and want to undo one or more of them click on the *Undo* icon. You may have to click several times to get back to the edit you want to undo. Alternatively, by clicking on *Edit* at the top of the screen you can find an *Undo edits* option, or you can use Ctrl + Z.

Saving the edited graph

Right click on the graph you have edited and select *Stop graph editor*. If you choose the name `myedits` the graph will be saved as `myedits.gph` in the working directory.

Close the graph window and check that you can get the graph back with

```
. graph use myedits
```

To continue editing just right-click the graph and select *Start Graph Editor*.

Help

For help while editing, click on *Help* at the top of the screen, and select *Graph Editor*. Alternatively see the *Stata Graphics Reference Manual* in the documentation.

Exercises

There are no exercises for this chapter, but you might like to try some of the exercises for Chapter 5 using the dialog boxes to produce the same graph commands, or the graph editor to produce the same graphs.

Chapter 7

More basic tools

In this chapter you will learn how to use the return list, how to generate random numbers, how to group the values of a metric variable, how to compare two means or proportions, how to use weights, how to repeat commands for different groups of observations using by and bysort, and how to repeat commands using foreach.

7.1 The return list

After each Stata command some of the results are stored in memory so that they can be referred to. For example, try

```
. use births, clear
. summarize bweight
. return list
```

The mean is returned in r(mean), the standard deviation in r(sd) the sum in r(sum), and the number of observations in r(N). To refer to the values, try

```
. display r(sum)
. display r(N)
```

For a more extensive return list try

```
. summarize bweight, detail
. return list
```

For a very brief one, try

```
. tabulate hyp sex
. return list
```

Returns are useful when you need the results from one command to be fed into a new command. For example, to create a new variable `dbw` that holds the difference between each baby's birth weight and the overall birth weight mean we could use

```
. summarize bweight
. generate dbw =  bweight - r(mean)
```

7.2   Generating variables using functions

Stata functions can be used with `generate` and in their simplest form look like

$$generate \ new\_var = fname(old\_var)$$

where *new_var* is the name of the new variable you wish to generate, *old_var* is a variable already in your data set, and *fname* is the name of the function. For example,

```
. generate sqrbw=sqrt(bweight)
```

It is important not to leave a space between the function name and the first parenthesis, otherwise Stata thinks *fname* is a variable name, not a function.

If you ask for help on functions by selecting *Stata command* from the *Help* menu, and typing functions, you will see that they are arranged in 8 groups, starting with mathematical functions. Some of the basic functions like `ln()` have already been introduced, but another useful one is `runiform()`, which produces random numbers between 0 and 1. Note that although `runiform()` is a function it does not require an argument but it still needs the parentheses (). Try

```
. generate u=runiform()
. list u
. cdfplot u
```

The cumulative distribution of u shows that its values are uniformly distributed. The function `normal()` returns the standard normal cumulative probability, and its inverse is `invnormal()`. To generate random numbers from a standardized normal distribution try

```
. generate un=rnormal()
. cdfplot un
```

Functions can also be used as part of expressions used with `generate`, as in

```
. generate x=sqrt(10)*runiform()
```

Another class of functions can be used with the command `egen` which stands for extensions to generate. These take the general form

$$egen \ new\_var = fname(old\_var)$$

However, it is not possible to use `egen` functions as part of expressions. Some examples of `egen` functions are shown in the next section. Ask for help on `egen` to see the list of available functions.

7.3 Grouping the values of a variable

When a variable has many values, like `matage`, it is often useful to group the values and to create a new variable which codes the groups. For example we might cut the values taken by `matage` into the groups 20–29, 30–34, 35–39, 40–44, and to create a new variable called `agegrp` coded 20 for subjects in the first age group, 30 for subjects in the second age group, 35 for subjects in the third age group, and so on, using the lower end of the age group as the code. The best way of doing this is to use `egen` with the function `cut`. Try

```
. egen agegrp=cut(matage), at(20,30,35,40,45)
. browse
```

You will see that the new variable `agegrp` takes the value 20 when `matage` is in the first age group, 30 when `matage` is in the second age group, and so on. The last group, consisting of values from 40 up to but not including 45, is coded 40.

The function `cut` offers a number of useful options. If you prefer to code the groups using the integer codes 0, 1, 2, . . . instead of 20, 30, 35, . . . try

```
. drop agegrp
. egen agegrp=cut(matage), at(20,30,35,40,45) icodes
. tab agegrp
```

It is necessary to drop `agegrp` first because `egen`, like `generate`, creates a new variable. To save some typing you could replace (20,30,35,40,45) with (20,30(5)45), both of which are examples of what Stata calls *number lists*.Try `help numlist` for a full list of which abbreviations are allowed in a number list.

You can also label the values of the categorical variable `agegrp` using

```
. drop agegrp
. egen agegrp=cut(matage), at(20,30(5)45) icodes label
. tabulate agegrp
```

It is important to realize that values which are not inside the range specified in the `at()` part of the command result in missing values for the new categorical variable. For example, try

```
. drop agegrp
. egen agegrp=cut(matage), at(20,30,35) icodes label
. tabulate agegrp
. tabulate agegrp, missing
```

Only values from 20 up to, but not including 35, are included. For the rest, `agegrp` is coded missing. If you don't want to choose the cut-points for the categories of `matage`, try

```
. drop agegrp
. egen agegrp=cut(matage), group(5)
. tabulate agegrp
```

which will produce 5 roughly equal–frequency groups coded 0, 1, 2, 3, 4. The option `label` will show the lower ends of the intervals in terms of the original units of `matage`. Try this option now (remember to drop `agegrp` first). To create a new variable, `agegrpm`, holding the mean value of `matage` corresponding to each category of `agegrp`, the `egen` function `mean` can be used. Try

```
. bysort agegrp: egen agegrpm=mean(matage)
. tabulate agegrpm
```

For a quick reference to the functions available with `egen`, try

```
. db egen
```

7.4   Comparing two means or two proportions

Testing the difference between two means using the t-test is a very basic statistical requirement, and will be illustrated by comparing the mean birth weight of the babies of hypertensive and normal mothers. The command

```
. ttest bweight, by(hyp)
```

shows an unusual amount of output for such a simple operation. The most important line in the table is the last which refers to the difference in the two means. The null hypothesis which is being tested is that the true values of the two means are equal, and the value of t and the corresponding two-sided p-value are shown at the bottom, mid-screen. The t is very large (5.455) and the p-value is small, so the difference is highly significant.

The proportions of low birth weight babies born to hypertensive and normal mothers are obtained with

```
. tabulate lowbw hyp, col
```

The proportions are 9% for normal mothers and 28% for hypertensive mothers. To test the significance of this difference use the option `chi2`:

```
. tabulate lowbw hyp, col chi2
```

The chi-squared statistic is large, and the p-value is small, so the difference is highly significant. Another way of making comparisons between means and proportions which generalizes to several groups is described in Chapter 11.

A few Stata commands are also available in an immediate form, so they can be used in calculator mode, with numbers instead of variables. For example, the test described above could also be carried out with

```
. tabi 388 52 \40 20, col chi2
```

See help for `immed` for a list of immediate commands in Stata.

7.5 Weights

In some data sets each observation has an associated weight. This might be a frequency weight which indicates that the observation occurred with a given frequency, or an importance weight which states that when calculating things like means the observation should be weighted by its importance. Frequency weights must be integers, but importance weights can be any numbers. There are two other kinds of weight in Stata which have a more specialised purpose, namely probability weights and analytical weights. See the *Stata User's Guide (Weighted estimation)* for a discussion of the different sorts of weight, or type `help weights`.

Most Stata commands can be used with weights. For example, suppose the births data consisted of just the variables `lowbw` and `hyp`. There are only four possibilities for the observations, namely

```
lowbw hyp
    0   0
    1   0
    0   1
    1   1
```

Rather than enter 500 observations of this kind, it would be better to enter the four observations

```
lowbw hyp     N
    0   0   388
    1   0    40
    0   1    52
    1   1    20
```

where the last variable, N, gives the frequency with which each combination occurs in the data. Such a data set is in the file `births_freq.dta`, so try

```
. use births_freq, clear
. tabulate lowbw hyp
```

This ignores the frequencies, and the table is based on just the 4 observations. To take the frequencies into account, try

```
. tabulate lowbw hyp [fw=N]
```

where `fw` stands for frequency weights. This shows that `tabulate` now understands that there are 500 observations in the data, not 4. Alternatively, the data can be expanded to individual observations, as follows:

```
. expand N
. drop N
. describe
```

There are now 500 observations. The command `expand N` works by replacing each observation with n copies where n is the value of the variable N for that observation. For example, for the first observation N takes the value 388, so the first observation is replaced by 388 copies of itself.

7.6 Repeating commands for different sub-groups

Stata has a powerful facility for processing observations by groups. For a straightforward example, load the births data and summarize the variable `bweight` in detail, for each hypertension group, as follows:

```
. use births, clear
. bysort hyp: summarize bweight, detail
```

Of course this could have been done just as easily with

```
. summarize bweight if hyp==0, detail
. summarize bweight if hyp==1, detail
```

but spelling out the different values of the variable which is defining the groups would get tedious with more than 3 or 4 values, and the `bysort` command can be used to automate this. The groups can also be defined by combinations of variables, as in

```
. bysort hyp sex: summarize bweight, detail
```

7.7 Repeating commands for different variables

Some Stata commands allow you to specify a list of variables, and will repeat the command for each variable. For example

```
. summarize matage bweight gestwks
```

summarizes each of the variables in the list. You could do the same thing with

```
. foreach var of varlist matage bweight gestwks {
. summarize 'var'
. }
```

Here `var` is a local macro [1] which contains each of the variable names `matage bweight gestwks` in turn. The curly brackets enclose the commands that will be repeated for each of these variable names. Any name can be used for the local macro. For example

---

[1] Macros are abbreviations for information. For example if the local macro named X contains the information "Wed 18 Jan", then 'X' is short for Wed 18 Jan.

```
. foreach X of varlist matage bweight gestwks {
. summarize 'X'
. }
```

would do as well.

The single quotes which surround `var` and `X` are important – the left hand single quote is different from the right hand one. On most keyboards you will find them on the top left-hand corner (below the *Esc* key) and near the *Enter* key of the keyboard, respectively. If you are using a non-English keyboard you may not find these keys. In this case it is best to allocate two of the function keys, as follows:

```
. macro define F4=char(96)
. macro define F5=char(39)
```

Now pressing F4 will produce the left-hand quote and F5 will produce the right-hand quote.

You can repeat several commands by enclosing them in the brackets { }, but each command must be typed on a new line, as in

```
. foreach var of varlist matage bweight gestwks {
. summarize 'var'
. count if missing('var')
. }
```

Stata prints a line number for each new line, a process which stops with the last }.

You can also use 'var' within the text displayed by `display` as in

```
. foreach var of varlist matage bweight gestwks {
. quietly summarize 'var'
. display as result "Mean of variable 'var' is  " r(mean)
. }
```

The prefix `quietly` before a command prevents all output except error messages.

The keyword `varlist` is used to indicate a list of existing variables. If you want to create new variables the keyword is `newlist`. For example,

```
. foreach var of newlist tom dick harry {
. generate 'var' = bweight
. }
. list tom dick harry in 1/10
```

will generate 3 copies of `bweight` called `tom`, `dick`, and `harry`.

The command `foreach` also works with lists of numbers when the keyword `numlist` is used. Try

```
. foreach num of numlist 1,2,3 {
```

```
. generate bw`num'=bweight
. }
. list bw* in 1/10
```

which creates three new variables `bw1-bw3`, each a copy of `bweight`. Make sure there is no space between `bw` and `'num'`. Their names are made of the common root `bw` followed by one of the numbers in `numlist`.

These examples refer to different kinds of list – `varlist` refers to existing variable names, `newlist` refers to new variable names, and `numlist` refers to a Stata number list. Using the syntax `of varlist`, or `of newlist`, or `of numlist` enables Stata to carry out some rudimentary checks, for example that the list of names in a `varlist` are all existing variable names. A looser syntax can be used with any kind of list. For example,

```
. foreach var in matage bweight gestwks {
. summarize `var'
. }
```

will have the same effect as

```
. foreach var of varlist matage bweight gestwks {
. summarize `var'
. }
```

without the checks. This more general kind of list is useful with file names. Try

```
. foreach file in births dates {
. use `file' , clear
. summarize
. }
```

Each of the data files is loaded and summarized, in turn. Note that the keyword `of` was used for lists of variables and numbers, but `in` is used for a general list such as one of file names.

Exercises

1. Load the births data and create a new variable `gest4` which cuts `gestwks` at 20, 35, 37, 39, 45 weeks using `egen`.

2. Obtain a frequency table for the categorical variable `gest4` using `tabulate`.

3. Obtain a table of mean birth weight by categories of `gest4`, using `table`.

4. Create a new variable `diffma` equal to the difference between `matage` and the overall mean of `matage` using `r(mean)`.

5. Create a new variable equal to the square root of `bweight`.

6. Use `bysort` to summarize `bweight` for each value of `sex`.

7. Create the categorical variable `mage4` from `matage` using `egen` with the function `cut` and the options `group(4)` and `label`. Tabulate `mage4`: what are the quartiles used to group `matage`?

8. Test whether the birth weight means of boys and girls are significantly different using the command `ttest`.

9. Tabulate each of the variables `hyp`, `sex` and `preterm` using the command `foreach`.

10. Summarize, take logs, and then summarize the log-transformed variable, for each variable in the list `matage gestwks bweight`, using `foreach`. You can either replace each variable by its log transform (bad practice) or create a new variable, say `log'var'`, to hold the log transformed variable before summarizing.

Chapter 8

Data management

In this chapter you will learn how to clean data; how to append one data file to another; how to merge data files, and how to update one file with information from another.

8.1 Cleaning data

Cleaning data means eliminating any errors which occurred while the data were being collected or computerized. It involves making checks on the values which the variables take, and is best done with a do file. We shall give some examples of common checks, using the births data. The commands

```
. use births, clear
. summarize
```

can reveal some discrepancies, but more specific checks may be needed. To check that sex takes only the values 1, 2, or missing, we can count and identify any observations where this is not true with

```
. count if sex!=1 & sex!=2 & !missing(sex)
. list id sex if sex!=1 & sex!=2 & !missing(sex)
```

We have excluded missing values with !missing(sex) rather than sex!=. to make sure that all missing codes are excluded. The result of the first command should be 0 if sex is coded correctly; the result of the second should list the id and the value for sex for any subjects who have been incorrectly coded. Let us recode sex as 3 for subject 10, and run the checks again:

```
. replace sex=3 if id==10
. count if    sex!=1 & sex!=2 & !missing(sex)
. list id sex if   sex!=1 & sex!=2 & !missing(sex)
```

Once an error has been detected it can be corrected using the command `replace`.

To check that `gestwks` lies in the range 20–44 if it is not missing, count the observations for which `gestwks` is less than 20 or greater than 44 and not missing, as follows:

```
. count if gestwks<20 | gestwks>44 & !missing(gestwks)
```

It is always important to bear in mind the possibility that a value may be missing when carrying out checks. If it is missing remember that the missing value codes for numeric data are treated as very large numbers, so in this example a missing value for `gestwks` would be greater than 44.

Duplicate observations can be a problem and are best dealt with using the command `duplicates`. For example,

```
. duplicates report
```

shows there are no duplicate observations in the `births` data set, but it is easy to insert some with

```
. expand 3 in 1/2
```

which makes 2 copies of each of the first two observations. The command `duplicates report` now shows that there are 6 observations which have 3 copies, 4 of which are surplus. The command `duplicates list` lists all 6 observations, and

```
. duplicates drop
```

will drop the 4 surplus observations. The `duplicates` command can refer to a subset of variables. For example

```
. duplicates report id
```

will check that identity numbers are unique.

8.2   String variables

String variables are more difficult to deal with than numeric variables because there are so many more possibilities with strings than with numbers. Fortunately there are good functions in Stata which help with managing string variables. To illustrate some of these, load and list the data in the file `string.dta` with

```
. use string, clear
. list
```

The variable `name` contains the names of three subjects. To sort on `name` try

```
. sort name
```

Sorting on a string variable sorts in alphabetical order with capital letters preceding small letters. To create a new string variable containing the name in upper case, try

```
. generate name1=upper(name)
. list
```

The variable **name** contains the first and second names of each subject. We shall now separate the first name from the second and put them together in the opposite order. Start by finding where the blank occurs with

```
. generate b=strpos(name, " ")
```

The variable **b** contains the position where a blank character first occurs in the variable **name**. Now we can use the **substr** function to separate the first name (from 1 to $b-1$) from the last name (from $b+1$ to the end). Try

```
. generate first=substr(name,1,b-1)
. generate last =substr(name,b+1,.)
. list
```

where **substr(name,b+1,.)** extracts the string from $b+1$ to the end, wherever that might be. Finally, to put them together in the opposite order, separated by a comma, try

```
. generate name2=last + ", " + first
. list
```

For some commands, where a string variable is not allowed, it is useful to create a numeric variable which takes the value 1 for the first combination of string characters, 2 for the second, and so on. Identical strings are coded with the same number. The command to do this for the variable **name** is

```
. encode name, gen(namecode)
. list name namecode
```

where **namecode** is the numeric variable which contains numerical codes in place of the strings. At first sight it seems that nothing has changed because the values of **namecode** have been labelled with the values of **name**. Try

```
. list name namecode, nolab
```

to convince yourself that **namecode** is numerical, and note that the codes have been allocated in the alphabetic order of the names.

Finally, it is worth mentioning that any number such as 24 can be coded numerically, or as the string composed of the character 2 and the character 4. It sometimes happens that a variable contains numbers as strings, which can be most confusing. When the variable is listed the values look like numbers, but they are not. However, they can easily be converted to numbers using the function **real()** or the command **destring**. For more information about string functions try

70

```
. help strfun
```

or look up *strings* in the *Stata User's Guide (Strings)*.

8.3 Appending to add more observations

Data are often collected separately and stored in different files. The separate files are then appended to each other to form a single file. To illustrate the `append` command we shall start with the file `agesex.dta` which contains

id	age	sex
100	47	m
101	.	f
102	67	m

and append the file `newsubj.dta` which contains

id	age	sex
103	22	m

with the following commands

```
. clear
. append using agesex newsubj
. list
```

8.4 Merging to add more variables

Another way of collecting data is to store different kinds of information in different files, and then to merge the files using one or more variables as *key* variables. In a 1:1 merge the key variables uniquely identify the observations in both files. As an example we shall merge the file `agesex.dta` with the file `employ.dta` which contains information on a new variable `employed`:

id	employed
100	yes
101	yes
102	no

The key variable which uniquely identifies the subjects in both files is `id`. To merge the files, one file must be in memory and the other must be on disk in Stata format (`.dta`). Now try

```
. use agesex, clear
. merge 1:1 id using employ
. list
```

The file in memory before the merge (`agesex.dta`) is called the *master* file while the file on disk with which it is to be merged (`employ.dta`) is called the *using* file. The `list` command shows a new variable called `_merge`. This is created by Stata whenever the command `merge` is used, unless you specify the `nogenerate` option. It takes the values:

1 when the observation is only from the master file
2 when the observation is only from the using file
3 when the observation is from both.

To see this more clearly try

```
. list, nolabel
```

In this case the value is 3 for all subjects. The `merge` command automatically tabulates this new variable, even when it is not generated, to show how many observations of each type you have. If you have generated `_merge` you must drop it before any additional merges otherwise an error message will appear when the new merge tries to create it. Another useful option is `keep`, so that `keep(3)` keeps only observations which have matches in both the master and using data sets.

8.5   m:1 and 1:m merges

When merging the `agesex` file using the `employ` file the key variable, `id`, uniquely identified the observations in both files, but this is not always the case. For example, in a typical repeated measurement study, data which do not change with time, such as sex and age at entry, are collected in one file, while data which do change with time, such as blood pressure, are collected as one observation per visit in another file.

As an example, the file `agesex.dta` contains information for three subjects:

id	age	sex
100	47	m
101	.	f
102	67	m

while the file `bp.dta` contains data on blood pressure for each visit to a clinic:

id	visit	bp
100	1	180
100	2	160
100	3	155
101	1	160
102	1	120
102	2	140

so the first file holds subject-level information while the second one holds visit-level information. In the first file the key variable `id` uniquely identifies the observations, But in the second file there are many observations for each value of the key variable. To merge the files requires a 1:m merge, as in:

```
. use agesex, clear
. merge 1:m id using bp
. sort id visit
. list
```

You will see that in the merged files there are several observations for the same `id`, each containing both subject-level and visit-level information:

id	age	sex	visit	bp	_merge
100	47	m	1	180	3
100	47	m	2	160	3
100	47	m	3	155	3
101	.	f	1	160	3
102	67	m	1	120	3
102	67	m	2	140	3

The roles of the two files can be interchanged and merged with a m:1 merge.

When `1:1` is specified in a merge, the command checks whether the key variables uniquely determine the observations in both the master and using data sets, and gives an error message if they do not. Similarly, when `1:m` is specified the command checks that the key variables uniquely determine the observations in the master data set, but not the using data set. To demonstrate this try

```
. use agesex, clear
. expand 2
. merge 1:1 id using employ
```

which gives an error message. Similarly

```
. merge 1:m id using employ
```

gives an error message, but

```
. merge m:1 id using employ
. list
```

succeeds.

8.6   Merging to update variables

Another use of `merge` is to update the information on some of the variables in a data set. For example, the age for subject 101 is missing in `agesex.dta`. Suppose

we wished to update this missing value with the correct age, which is in the file
`age101.dta` containing

```
 id       age
101        32
```

A single correction of this kind could be done more easily with the command `replace`,
but `merge` would be useful when there were many values to update. Try

```
. use agesex, clear
. merge m:1 id using age101
. list
```

and you will see that nothing has changed! Stata carefully guards the master file
against change unless specifically authorized with the option `update`. Now try

```
. use agesex, clear
. merge m:1 id using age101, update
. list
```

and you will see that the missing value for age has been replaced with its updated
value. When `update` is used the variable `_merge` takes additonal values 4, 5:

4 for an observation from both files, missing in master updated
5 for an observation from both files, master disagrees with using file.

In the last of these cases the master would not be updated. Only when the master
value is missing it is updated. If you want to update the master in spite of the
disagreement, use the options `update` and `replace` together.

Exercises

1. The file `births_bad.dta` contains the same data as `births.dta`, but with some errors. Can you find them?

2. The file `music.dta` contains the musical skills for 10 subjects. List the `id` for all subject who play the piano. List the `id` for all subjects who play the flute. List the `id` for all subjects who do not play the piano.

3. Data on smoking habits for the mother of the babies in the births data set are contained in the file `births_smok.dta`. No data are available for 4 women, so the file has 496 observations. Start by loading and describing the file `births_smok.dta`.

4. How many ever-smokers are there? What is the mean age at which ever-smokers started smoking?

5. Merge the file `births.dta` with `births_smok.dta` using `id` as the key variable. How many women in the study did not have smoking information.

6. List the identifiers for all mothers without smoking information.

Chapter 9

Data management for repeated measurements

Repeated measurement data are also known as panel data, and as longitudinal data. In this chapter you will learn how to use long coding for repeated measurements; how to graph repeated measurements; how to collapse to group level; and how to work at group level without collapsing.

9.1 Wide and long coding

Consider the situation where repeated measurements of one or more variables are made on a subject at different time points during the study. If a variable X is measured on 3 occasions the results could be recorded as a single observation

id	X_1	X_2	X_3
1	x	x	x

or as 3 separate observations

id	X	visit
1	x	1
1	x	2
1	x	3

The first of these, where there is a new variable for the measurement at each time point, is called wide coding. The second, where there is one variable for the measurement and one for the time point, is called long coding. Another example of long coding, which does not involve time, is in family studies where a measurement is made on each member of a family. In wide coding there would be a measurement variable for each member of the family

family	X_1	X_2	X_3	X_4
1	x	x	x	x

whereas in long coding there would be one variable for the measurement X and one for the place in the family:

family	member	X
1	1	x
1	2	x
1	3	x
1	4	x

Data on forced expiratory volume (FEV) as a percentage of normal, measured every 3 months over a period of 48 months, are coded long in the file `fevlong.dta`, and wide in `fevwide.dta`. To see the difference

```
. describe using fevlong
. describe using fevwide
```

9.2   Graphing repeated measures

For the FEV data it would be helpful to see a graph of forced expiratory volume by month, for each subject. To obtain the graph for subject 1, for example, try

```
. use fevlong, clear
. sort id month
. twoway connected fev month if id==1
```

Each observation is connected to the next one in the file, so the file needs to be sorted by `id`, then `month` within `id`. To see the graphs for all subjects in group 3, try (expect a long wait here)

```
. twoway connected fev month if grp==3, by(id)
```

This shows a separate graph for each subject. To see the graphs for all subjects in group 3 on the same graph, try

```
. twoway connected fev month if grp==3, connect(ascending)
```

The option `connect(ascending)` tells Stata to connect each point to the next provided that the X-values are ascending – in this case provided that the month is ascending. When the data are sorted by `id` and `month`, this has the effect of joining the points until the month changes back to 0, i.e. until the subject `id` changes. If the data are not correctly sorted the connecting lines in the graph are all over the place. For example, try

```
. generate u=runiform()
. sort u
. twoway connected fev month if grp==3, c(ascending)
```

and you will see a tangle of lines.

9.3   Working at the group level

The graphs above are at the subject level, but it might be interesting to see the plot of mean FEV against month by grp. This can be done by using the egen command

```
. egen mfev=mean(fev), by(grp month)
```

to create the means by group and month. To see the result of the egen command, try

```
. sort grp month id
. browse
```

You will see that the new variable mfev, which contains the mean FEV by group and month, takes a value for each subject but for subjects in the same group and month these values are the same. To graph the means for the three groups try

```
. sort grp month id
. twoway connected mfev month, c(ascending)
```

At first sight this is surprising, because we have plotted the graphs using data on the subjects, yet the graphs are at group level. The reason for this is that the same graph is being plotted for each subject in group 3, and similarly for groups 1 and 2, so the graphs appear as one per group.

9.4   Collapsing the data

The collapse command can be used to create a new data set which contains the mean FEV by group and month. Try

```
. use fevlong, clear
. collapse (mean) mfev=fev, by(grp month)
. describe
. list
```

The data are still coded long, but the unit of observation is now the group-month not the subject-month, and there are only 41 observations. The syntax of the collapse command needs a little explanation: the (mean) mfev=fev asks for a new variable called mfev which contains the mean of the existing variable fev. The by(grp month) asks for the means to be calculated by group and month, and for the variables grp and month to be retained in the collapsed data set. To graph the group means in the collapsed data try

```
. sort grp month
. twoway connected mfev month, c(ascending)
```

Other possibilities for `collapse` include `(median)`, `(sum)`, `(max)`, `(min)`, etc. For a full list with examples, try `help collapse`.

9.5   Reshaping from long to wide and vice versa

Long coding is more versatile than wide, but with wide coding it is easier to make comparisons between different variables. For example, with family data it would be easier to compare the family members with wide coding than with long coding. Fortunately there is a command which will convert from long to wide, or from wide to long.

The information about `fev` is coded long in `fevlong.dta`, and can be converted to wide coding with the command

```
. use fevlong, clear
. reshape wide fev, i(id) j(month)
. describe
```

The `i()` option contains the variable which identifies the subject, while the `j()` option refers to the variable which contains the month in which the measurement took place.[1] The variable `fev`, which is being converted from long to wide, follows the keyword `wide`, and the names of the new variables which make up the columns in the wide coding are made up by combining `fev` with the values of `month` to give `fev0`, `fev3`, etc. After the `reshape wide` command you will see more variables and fewer observations. You can now convert from wide to long and long to wide, as often as you wish, with

```
. reshape long
. describe
. reshape wide
. describe
```

Now suppose we started with wide coding. The FEV data are also coded wide in the file `fevwide.dta`, where the observations look like this:

```
id  grp   fev0    fev3    fev6  ...   fev48
 1    1   60.58   65.35   55.87 ...   65.68
```

To convert to long, try

```
. use fevwide, clear
. reshape long fev, i(id) j(month)
. describe
```

---

[1]Mathematicians commonly use the symbols i for rows (subjects) and j for columns (variables), which explains why they are used here.

The name within the round brackets in j( ) refers to a variable that did not exist in `fevwide` but is created for the long format and takes the numerical information which follows fev in `fev0`, `fev3,fev6`, ..., `fev48`. Try `help reshape` for further details and examples.

9.6 Use of system variables with by:

The system variable `_n` indexes each observation in turn, from 1 to `_N`, where `_N` is the total number of observations. Try

```
. use fevlong, clear
. count
. display _N
. generate row = _n
. browse row id month
```

and you will see that the variable `row` takes the value 1 for the first observation, 2 for the second, and so on up to the last. When used with `by` the variable `_n` refers to the observations in each group defined by the `by`, and the variable `_N` refers to the total number of observations in each group. For example, for the observations in a group of 3 observations, defined by a variable `grp` taking the value 1, the variables `_n` and `_N` take the values:

grp	_n	_N
1	1	3
1	2	3
1	3	3

To illustrate some of the uses of these two system variables, we shall first generate a new variable `visits` which records the number of times each subject visits the clinic for an FEV measurement, try

```
. sort id
. by id: generate visits = _N
. browse
```

For each value of `id` the variable `visits` takes as its value the number of observations for that `id`, i.e. the number of visits. You will see that subject 1 makes 15 visits, and that the variable `visits` has been given the value 15 for each of the 15 observations on subject 1. If you tabulate `visits` with

```
. tabulate visits
```

the total frequency is 663, the number of observations, not the number of subjects, which is 57.

The best way of making the table of values of visits refer to subjects is to create the variable only for the first observation for each subject. This is done by using _n to restrict the generate command to the first observation:

```
. drop visits
. by id: generate visits = _N if _n == 1
. browse
```

You will see that visits takes the value 15 for the first observation for subject 1, but is missing for the others. Now try

```
. tabulate visits
```

which tabulates the frequency of visits made by each subject: six subjects makes 3 visits, one subject makes 4 visits, etc.

As another example, suppose we wish to create a variable up which measures the increase in FEV from 0 to 3 months. To do this, try

```
. sort id month
. by id: generate up = fev - fev[_n-1]
. browse
```

Note the use of fev[_n-1] which refers to the previous observation – for this to work, the data must be sorted by id then month within id. Another way of doing this is with bysort:

```
. drop up
. bysort id (month): generate up = fev - fev[_n-1]
. browse
```

The parentheses around month indicate that the sort is on both id and month but the by refers only to id.

Exercises

1. Most countries publish mortality rates, separately for each 5-year age-band, every five years. The file `lungcalong.dta` contains the mortality rates for lung cancer, for males in Finland, coded long. Load this file and list its contents. Each observation corresponds to an age group, and a calendar period, and contains a single rate per 100 000. This is long coding. Graph the rate against period, separately for each age group, using a log scale for the rate. You can do this by using the option `yscale(log)` with `twoway connected`. Give careful thought to how the data should be sorted.

2. Change the marker label to the code for age group by using the option `mlabel(age)`. Label the Y-axis in a better way.

3. Graph the rate against age group, separately for each period, using a log scale for the rate. Use the code for period as the marker label.

4. The code for period takes up too much space, so create a new code

   ```
   . generate pcode=(period-1970)/5
   ```

   and use `pcode` as the marker label.

5. Most commonly, data of this kind are first coded wide, with the rates for all age-bands included in a single observation. This is illustrated in the file `lungcawide.dta`. Load this file and list its contents.

6. To reshape this as long, try

   ```
   . reshape long rate, i(period) j(age)
   . describe
   ```

   Note that the variable `age` takes the numerical information following `rate` while `period` refers to the current (wide) observations, one for each period.

7. Load the data in `fevwide` and remind yourself of its contents. Use `reshape long` to create a new variable called `ratio` which is the ratio between the first and last FEV measurements for each subject.

Chapter 10

Response and explanatory variables

In this chapter we shall start by considering how variables are to be used in a statistical analysis. The main distinction is between response and explanatory variables. The type of response carries useful information about how to summarize the distribution of the response in tables.

10.1 Questions in statistical analysis

Most questions in statistical analysis take the form of asking whether the value which one variable takes for a given subject depends on the value taken by another variable. For example, in the births data we might be interested in whether the birth weight of a baby depends on whether it is a boy or girl. The variable which is of primary interest, in this case the birth weight, is called the response variable; the variable on which the response variable may depend, in this case the sex of the baby, is called the explanatory variable. In biostatistics four types of response are particularly common:

1. Binary

2. Metric

3. Failure

4. Count

A binary response has just two values which should be coded 0 and 1. A metric response (also called a quantitative response) measures some quantity and usually has many possible values. A failure response indicates whether or not a subject fails at the end of a period under study, and is used with survival data. Finally, a count response records a number of events, and often arises with aggregated failure data. The type of response determines how it will be summarized. For example, a binary response is usually summarized using the proportion of 1's, and a metric response is usually summarized using its mean or median. The following questions illustrate response and explanatory variables and refer to the births data.

Does the birth weight of a baby depend on whether the mother was hypertensive?

The response variable is `bweight` which is metric and the explanatory variable is `hyp`. Because the response is metric the distribution of response can be summarized using either the mean or the median. Such a table of means, for example, can be produced with the commands

```
. use births, clear
. table hyp, contents(count bweight mean bweight)
```

Does low birth weight depend on the sex of the baby?

The response variable is now `lowbw` which is binary and the explanatory variable is `sex`. The distribution of `lowbw` by `sex` is given by the relative frequencies of its values, obtained with

```
. tabulate lowbw sex, col
```

which shows that 10% of male babies are of low birth weight, while 14% of female babies are of low birth weight. The `table` command is meant primarily for summarizing a metric response, but it can be used with a binary response provided that this is coded 0/1. Thus

```
. table sex, contents(count lowbw mean lowbw)
```

again shows that 10% of male babies are of low birth weight, while 14% of female babies are of low birth weight. This works because the mean of a variable coded 0/1 is equal to the relative frequency of the 1's.

10.2 Producing tables with tabmore

To help in the preparation of tables for a variety of responses a dialog box called up by the command `db tabmore`[1] invites you first to specify the type of response. Consider again the question of whether `bweight` varies with `hyp` and try

```
. db tabmore
```

---

[1] The command `tabmore` is not part of official Stata, and is not on the SSC site, but it is included with the files which come with this book (see Chapter 0).

to bring up the dialog box.

- Enter `bweight` in the *Response variable* box, select *metric* in the *Type of response* menu, and enter `hyp` in the *Row variable* box.

- Select the *Summary* tab. The response `bweight` is metric, and under metric you are offered three possibilities for summarizing the response - *Mean, Geometric mean,*, and *Median*. Select *Mean*, and press *OK* to produce

```
. tabmore, res(bweight) typ(metric) row(hyp) mean
```

The output looks like this:

```
Response variable is: bweight which is metric
Row variable is: hyp
Number of observations used:   500

Summary using means
----------------------
hypertens |    bweight
----------+-----------
       0 |    3198.90
       1 |    2768.21
----------------------
```

The figures in the table are the mean birth weights for mothers who were normal (`hyp=0`) or hypertensive (`hyp=1`). To get more information you could select the *More output* tab where you can select *Frequencies and Confidence intervals*. Try this now.

With a binary response, such as `lowbw`, the choice of summary is different. Try

```
. db tabmore
```

to bring up the dialog box, and press R to clear previous selections.

- Enter `lowbw` in the *Response variable* box, select *binary* as the *Type of response*, and enter `hyp` in the *Row variable* box.

- Select the *Summary* tab. Because the response is binary you will be offered a choice between *Proportions* and *Odds*. Select *Proportions* and press *OK* to produce

```
. tabmore, res(lowbw) typ(binary) row(hyp) prop
```

The output looks like this:

```
Response variable is: lowbw which is binary
Row variable is: hyp
Number of observations used:   500

Summary using proportions per 100
----------------------
hypertens |     lowbw
----------+-----------
        0 |      9.35
        1 |     27.78
----------------------
```

The figures in the table are the percentages of low birth weight babies for mothers who were normal or hypertensive. To produce 90% confidence intervals for these proportions, check *Confidence intervals* in the *More output* tab of the dialog box, and enter 90 in the *Level of confidence* box. Press *OK* to produce

```
. tabmore, res(lowbw) typ(binary) row(hyp) prop ci level(90)
```

The command can be edited, so small changes can be made without going through the dialog box again.

10.3   A second explanatory variable

We found a strong relationship between birth weight and whether the mother was hypertensive, but is this relationship the same for both male and female babies? To study this we need to produce a table of mean birth weight by both hyp and sex:

```
. table hyp sex, contents(count bweight mean bweight)
```

shows that the birth weight of both male and female babies is lower when the mother is hypertensive than when the mother is normal – about 500 g lower for males babies and about 400 g for female babies.

To produce the same table using tabmore, start with

```
. db tabmore
```

and press R to clear previous selections. Then enter bweight as *Response variable* and select *metric* as *Type*. Enter hyp as *Row variable*, and sex as *Column variable*. Select the *Summary* tab, select *Mean*, and press *OK* to produce

```
. tabmore, res(bweight) typ(metric) row(hyp) col(sex) mean
```

To reverse the rows and columns, check the box in the *Main* dialog box marked *Reverse rows and cols.*

10.4 Odds

Odds are less familiar than proportions, but they measure essentially the same thing. When 60 babies out of 500 are low birth weight the proportion is $60/500 = 0.12$, while the odds of being low birth weight are $60/440 = 0.1364$. The interpretation of the proportion 0.12 is that for every 100 babies, 12 are low birth weight; the interpretation of the odds 0.1364 is that for every 100 normal birth weight babies there will be 13.64 low birth weight babies. Odds can be obtained from proportions using

$$\text{Odds} = \frac{\text{Proportion}}{1 - \text{Proportion}} = \frac{0.12}{1 - 0.12} = 0.1364$$

Similarly proportions can be obtained from odds using

$$\text{Proportion} = \frac{\text{Odds}}{1 + \text{Odds}} = \frac{0.1364}{1 + 0.1364} = 0.12$$

Odds are always used with case-control studies (see Section 10.5), but also crop up with *logistic regression* (see Chap 13) where they have some technical advantages because they are not constrained to be less than 1, as proportions are. To make a table of the odds of the baby being low birth weight for normal and hypertensive mothers, start with

```
. db tabmore
```

and press R to remove previous selections. Enter `lowbw` as *Response variable*, and select *binary* as *Type*. Enter `hyp` as *Row variable*, select *Summary* and check *Odds*. Press *OK* to produce

```
. tabmore, res(lowbw) typ(binary) row(hyp) odds
```

Tables with too many rows are not particularly useful, and for this reason an upper limit of 10 values for the row and column variables has been set in `tabmore`. This can be increased in the *Main* tab, if required.

10.5 Case-control studies

Odds are important in case-control studies where, instead of sampling all subjects equally, a different sampling fraction is used for subjects who have a disease (the cases) than for those who do not (the controls). This is called *outcome-based sampling* in econometrics. As an example, we shall look at a study of physical activity at work and tuberculosis (TB), one of the first case-control studies to be carried out (see Table 10.1). The cases were cases of TB among outpatients at a hospital, and the controls were chosen from outpatients at the same hospital, who were not suffering from TB[7]. Start by listing the data in the file `guy.dta` with

87

Table 10.1: Physical activity at work for 1659 outpatients

Level of physical activity	Tuberculosis (Cases)	Other diseases (Controls)
Little (1)	125	385
Varied (2)	41	136
More (3)	142	630
Great (4)	33	167
Total	341	1318

```
. use guy, clear
. list, sep(0)
. list, sep(0) nolabel
```

The variable activity is coded 1, 2, 3, 4 for the four levels of physical activity, and the variable d is coded 1 for a case and 0 for a control. The data are aggregated, and the variable N contains the frequency with which each combination of activity and d occurs. One way of dealing with data of this kind is to make it into individual observations with the command expand:

```
. expand N
. drop N
. summarize
```

The variable N is dropped after the expansion because it is no longer relevant. There are now two possible approaches to the analysis (Clayton & Hills, 1993[2]). In the *retrospective* approach we argue from disease back to exposure so the response is activity, and the explanatory variable is d. The values of activity are measuring physical activity on some sort of metric scale, so we shall treat activity as metric.

Bring up the dialog box for tabmore and press R to remove previous selections. Enter activity as *Response variable*, and select *metric* as *Type*. Enter d as *Row variable*, select *Summary* and check *mean*. Press *OK* to produce

```
. tabmore, res(activity) typ(metric) row(d) mean
```

You should see something like

```
Summary using means

       d |        activity
---------+------------
       0 |        2.44
       1 |        2.24
```

which shows that cases of TB were, on average, less physically active than controls. In the *prospective* approach we argue from exposure forward to disease so the response is d, which is binary, and the explanatory variable is `activity`.

Bring up the dialog box for `tabmore` and press R to remove previous selections. Enter d as *Response variable*, and select *binary* as *Type*. Enter `activity` as *Row variable*, select *Summary* and check *odds*. Press *OK* to produce

```
. tabmore, res(d) typ(binary) row(activity) odds
```

and you should see something like

```
Summary using odds per 100
activity   |           d
-----------+-----------
    little |       32.47
    varied |       30.15
      more |       22.54
     great |       19.76
```

which shows that the odds of being a case decreases with the level of physical activity. Both retrospective and prospective analyses are useful, but on the whole the prospective one is more informative.

Note that the odds which are being tabulated refer to the odds of being a case in the study, not the population. However, it can be shown that

$$\text{Odds in study} = K \times \text{Odds in population},$$

where K is the ratio between the sampling fractions for cases and controls. So provided the sampling fractions do not depend on `activity`, it follows that if the study odds are going down with `activity`, then the population odds are also going down with `activity`. See Clayton & Hills (1993), p153[2] for a more detailed discussion of this point.

Now you can see why odds are chosen for the analysis of case-control studies: suppose that, instead of 1318 controls, there had been 10 times as many; the odds would now be (apart from random variation),

```
Summary using odds per 100
activity   |           d
-----------+-----------
    little |       3.247
    varied |       3.015
      more |       2.254
     great |       1.976
```

So although the odds have changed drastically because of the change in sampling the controls, the trend in the odds with `activity` is unchanged.

10.6 Survival data and rates

Data involving survival times are often summarized using *rates*, i.e. the number of events per unit time. There are no survival time variables in the births data, so we need another data set to demonstrate how to make tables of rates. Try

```
. use diet, clear
. describe
```

These data refer to a follow–up study of 337 male subjects who were asked to weigh the different components of their diet for a week[11]. They were then followed until

1. They developed, and possibly died from, coronary heart disease (CHD)

2. They died from some other cause, or were withdrawn from the study for some reason, or the study ended.

In the first case the time for which each subject is followed is the time before the subject develops CHD and is known as the *survival time*. In the second case follow-up stops before the subject develops CHD and the survival time is said to have been censored before the true survival time could be observed. To record data with censored survival times we need two variables: the time spent in the study and a variable which indicates whether the subject developed CHD or not. These are called the *follow-up* and *failure* variables, respectively.

In this example the follow-up variable is y, and the failure variable is chd, coded 1 if the subject developed CHD during the period of the study, and 0 otherwise. For a preliminary analysis the total energy intake per day is converted to a binary variable hieng coded 1 if the energy intake is > 2750 kcal, and 0 otherwise. To create a table of rates for chd by hieng, try

```
. db tabmore
```

and press R to remove previous selections. Then enter chd as *Response variable*, select *failure* as *Type* and enter y as *Follow-up time*. Enter hieng as the *Row variable*, select the *Summary* tab and check *Rates per 1000*. Press *OK* to produce

```
. tabmore, res(chd) typ(failure) row(hieng) rate fup(y)
```

Note that with rates the failure variable is selected as response. Rather unexpectedly, eating a lot seems to prevent CHD (7.07 compared with 13.60). This is because what you eat is largely determined by your physical activity, and a high level of physical activity helps prevent CHD.

10.7 Count data and rates

An example where the response variable is a count arises in the mortality data taken from Rothman (1986)[13]. These data refer to the total deaths and populations in 1962 in Panama and Sweden, by three age categories. Load the data with

```
. use mortality, clear
. describe
. list, sepby(nation)
```

The data are aggregated, so the response is the total number of deaths in each age–country category, which is in the variable `deaths`. Like failure data, count data also requires a follow-up time, and assuming each subject is followed for the whole of 1962, this is equal to the population multiplied by 1, which is the same as the variable `pop`. To find the mortality rate by nation using `tabmore`, try

```
. db tabmore
```

and press R to remove previous selections. Then enter `deaths` as *Response variable*, select *count* as *Type*, and enter `pop` as *Follow-up time*. Enter `nation` as *Row variable*, select the *Summary* tab, and check *Rates per 1000*. Press *OK* to produce

```
. tabmore, res(deaths) typ(count) row(nation) rate fup(pop)
```

The output shows that the overall (crude) mortality for Sweden is slightly higher than for Panama. A rather more accurate comparison is made by including `agegrp` as the column variable:

```
. tabmore, res(deaths) typ(count) row(nation) col(agegrp) rate fup(pop)
```

Now it is clear that in the first two age groups the mortality for Sweden is lower than the mortality for Panama. Only in the third age group is it higher.

10.8   Epitab

Stata has a suite of commands specifically for epidemiology (see `help epitab`). For the most part these stem from a time when analysis of epidemiological data was carried out by hand using a calculator, and are not integrated into the main stream of statistical models. For this reason they are omitted from this book.

Exercises

1. Start by loading the births data. Babies are classified as pre-term if they are born before 37 weeks. Does being pre-term depend on whether the mother is hypertensive or not? Prepare a table of proportions, with confidence intervals, to investigate this question using `tabmore`.

2. Does this relationship hold for both male and female babies? Investigate this by making a table of the proportion of pre-term babies by `hyp` and `sex`.

3. Does being pre-term change with maternal age? Investigate this by grouping the values of `matage` into a new variable, and preparing a table of proportions of pre–term babies by the categories of this new variable.

4. Repeat the previous table using odds in place of proportions; include 90% confidence intervals.

5. Load the diet data and prepare a table of rates per 1000, and confidence intervals, for `chd` by `job` using `tabmore`.

Chapter 11

Measuring effects

The word effect is a general term referring to ways of comparing the values of the response variable at different levels of an explanatory variable. This chapter covers the measurement of effects as

- Differences in means for a metric response.

- Differences in proportions for a binary response.

- Ratios of odds or proportions for a binary response.

- Ratios of rates for a failure response.

11.1 A metric response

In Chapter 10 we prepared a table of mean `bweight` by `hyp` using `tabmore`. This showed that hypertensive mothers had babies which were on average about 430 g smaller than those delivered to normal mothers. This difference in mean birth weight is called the *effect* of hypertension on birth weight. The command `db effects`, like `db tabmore`, brings up a dialog box which first invites you to specify the type of response.[1] When you bring up this dialog box you will see that the terms *exposure variable* and *stratifying variable* are used instead of *row variable* and *column variable*. The reason for this change is that when calculating effects it is important to distinguish between the different roles which the variables have in an analysis. The variable whose effects you want to calculate is called the *exposure* variable; *stratifying variables* will be introduced later in this chapter. In this example the response variable is `bweight` and the exposure variable is `hyp`, so try

---

[1] The command `effects` is not part of official Stata, and is not on the SSC site, but it is included with the files which come with this book (see Chapter 0).

```
. use births, clear
. db effects
```

then press R to clear previous selections.

- Enter `bweight` as *Response variable* and select *metric* as *Type*.

- Enter `hyp` as *Exposure*, and notice, at the bottom of the dialog box, that the exposure variable is treated as categorical by default.

- Select the *Measures of effect* tab, and check *Difference in means*. Press *OK* to produce

```
. effects, res(bweight) typ(metric) exp(hyp) exc md
```

The option `exc` states that the exposure is categorical. You will see that the effect of `hyp` on `bweight`, measured using the difference in the mean response, is -430.7 g. The 95% confidence interval for this effect is from -585 to -276 g. The statistical test is for the null hypothesis that the true effect of hypertension is zero, and is on 1 degree of freedom (df) because one effect is estimated. The p-value is very low so there is strong evidence against the null hypothesis. Tests of hypotheses are dealt with in more detail in Chapter 14.

To illustrate how to deal with a categorical exposure we shall cut `gestwks` into 4 groups with

```
. egen gest4=cut(gestwks), at(20,35,37,39,45)
. tabulate gest4
```

When comparing the mean birth weight between the four different levels of `gest4` there will be three effects: the effect comparing level 2 with level 1; level 3 with level 1; and level 4 with level 1. The level with which each of the other levels is compared is called the *baseline* (level 1 in this case). To prepare a table of the three effects of `gest4`, try

```
. db effects
```

then enter `gest4` as *Exposure* in place of `hyp`, and press *OK* to produce

```
. effects, res(bweight) typ(metric) exp(gest4) exc md
```

There are three effects, measured as differences in means, and the statistical test is for the null hypothesis that the true values of these effects are all zero is on 3 df because 3 effects are tested. The *Main* dialog allows you to change the baseline from its default value of 1. Try changing the baseline to 3: each of the levels 1, 2, 4 is now compared with level 3. This will add the option `base(3)` to the `effects` command.

94

11.2   A binary response

When examining the proportion of low birth weight babies according to the length of their gestation, using gestation time in four groups, each level of gest4 can be compared with the baseline level using the difference in proportions, or the ratio of proportions, or the odds ratio. The preferred method is to use the odds ratio.

Start by using tabmore to prepare a table of the odds that a baby has low birth weight, by the levels of gest4. Now try

```
. db effects
```

and press R to clear previous selections. Then enter lowbw as *Response variable* and select binary as *Type*. Enter gest4 as *Exposure*, select the *Measures of effect* tab, and check *Odds ratio*. Press *OK* to produce

```
. effects, res(lowbw) typ(binary) exp(gest4) exc or
```

You should see this table of three effects comparing levels 2, 3, 4 against level 1, using odds ratios:

```
Levels        Effect      95% Confidence Interval

2/1           0.164     [  0.05 ,   0.51 ]
3/1           0.029     [  0.01 ,   0.08 ]
4/1           0.003     [  0.00 ,   0.01 ]


Test for no effects

chi2(  3)      =  82.449
P-value        =   0.000
```

Compared with level 1 of gest4, mothers at level 2 have lower odds of a low birth weight baby by a factor of 0.164, mothers at level 3 have lower odds by a factor of 0.029, while mothers at level 4 have lower odds by a factor of 0.003. The statistical test that appears below the table is for the null hypothesis that the true values of these three effects (odds ratios) are all 1. It takes the form of a chi–squared statistic, and is on 3 df because there are three effects being tested.

This makes more sense if you choose level 4 as the baseline. The effects are then

```
Levels        Effect      95% Confidence Interval

1/4         356.944     [ 84.11 , 1514.78 ]
2/4          58.614     [ 15.36 ,  223.64 ]
3/4          10.349     [  3.00 ,   35.72 ]
```

Compared to women with gestation period greater than or equal to 39 weeks, the odds of having a low birth weight baby increase by a factor of 10.3 for women with gestation period in the range 37–39, by a factor of 58.6 for 35–37 and a factor of 357 for women with a gestation period less than 35 weeks. We have chosen to measure the effects of `gest4` as odds ratios, but they can also be measured using the ratios of proportions. Try

```
. db effects
```

select the *Measures of effect* tab, and check *Ratio of proportions*. You will see a table showing the three effects of `gest4` as ratios of proportions instead of odds ratios. You should be aware that when using the ratio or difference of proportions to measure effects, the program may fail to reach an answer when some of the proportions being compared are close to 0 or 1.

11.3   Case-control studies

For the measurement of effects in a prospective analysis of case-control studies it is essential to select odds ratios. Try

```
. use guy, clear
. expand N
. drop N
. db effects
```

and press R to clear previous selections. Then enter **d** as *Response variable* and select binary as *Type*. Enter `activity` as *Exposure*, select the *Measures of effect* tab, and check *Odds ratio*. Press *OK* to produce

```
. effects, res(d) typ(binary) exp(activity) exc or
```

You should see a table of odds ratios comparing levels 2/1, 3/1, and 4/1.

11.4   A failure response

Load the diet data and cut **energy** into 3 groups with

```
. use diet, clear
. egen eng3=cut(energy),at(1500,2500,3000,4500)
. tabulate eng3
```

Use `tabmore` to prepare a table showing the rates of CHD for different levels of `eng3`, and note that the rate goes down from 16.90 to 4.88 per 1000, with increasing levels of `eng3`. The two effects of `eng3` can be measured as rate differences or rate ratios. To prepare a table of effects using rate ratios, try

```
. db effects
```

and press R to clear previous selections. Then enter chd as *Response variable*, select failure as *Type*, and enter y as *Follow-up time*. Enter eng3 as *Exposure*, select the *Measures of effect* tab, and check *Rate ratio*. Press *OK* to produce

```
. effects, res(chd) typ(failure) exp(eng3) exc rr fup(y)
```

You should see something like this:

```
Levels        Effect    95% Confidence Interval

2/1           0.645    [  0.34 ,   1.23 ]
3/1           0.289    [  0.12 ,   0.67 ]


Test for no effects

chi2(  2)    =    8.241
P-value      =    0.016
```

Compared with level 1 of eng3, subjects at level 2 have a lower rate of CHD by a factor of 0.645, and subjects at level 3 have a lower rate of CHD by a factor of 0.289. The statistical test that appears below the table is for the null hypothesis that the true values of both effects of eng3 are 1. The p-value is very small, so there is strong evidence against the null hypothesis.

11.5   Metric exposure variables

When using tabmore no distinction is drawn between categorical and metric explanatory variables. If a metric variable such as gestwks in the births data is selected as explanatory, tabmore simply refuses to make a table because gestwks has too many values. When using effects the distinction between categorical and metric is essential because, as we shall now see, it is possible to find the effects of a metric exposure even when it has many values.

We shall illustrate this by finding the effect of gestwks on bweight. Even though gestwks has many values we can still find the effect of one unit increase in gestwks on bweight by making the assumption that this effect is the same throughout the range, i.e. that the effect of changing from 30 to 31 weeks of gestation is the same as changing from 31 to 32, and so on throughout the range. If this is the case then the relationship between bweight and gestwks is *linear*, so start by checking this with

```
. use births, clear
. twoway scatter bweight gestwks
```

You will see that birth weight tends to go up with gestational age, and that the increase in birth weight per unit increase in gestation (in weeks) is roughly constant throughout its range of values. To find the effect of a unit increase in gestwks, try

. db effects

and press R. Then select `bweight` as *Response variable* and metric as *Type*. Select
`gestwks` as *Exposure* and check the *Metric exposure* box. You are offered a choice for
the effect of a metric exposure as *per something*, but the default is per 1 unit, so go
with this. Select the *Measures of effect* tab and check *Difference in means.* and press
OK to produce

. effects, res(bweight) typ(metric) exp(gestwks) exm md

There is now only one effect, namely 197.0 g per unit increase in `gestwks`, i.e. per
week of gestation.

We can do the same thing to find the effect of `gestwks` on `lowbw`, using odds ratios
to measure the effect. We are now making the assumption that the odds of a low
birth weight baby has is reduced by the same factor for a change in gestation from 30
to 31 weeks, 31 to 32 weeks, and so throughout the range. This is the same as saying
that the relationship between the log odds and `gestwks` is linear. The easiest way to
check this is to cut `gestwks` into equally spaced groups[2] with

. egen gest3=cut(gestwks), at(30(5)45)

To look at how the odds change from one group to the next, try

. tabmore, res(lowbw) typ(binary) row(gest3) odds graph log

You can produce this command with the `tabmore` dialog box if you prefer. You will see
that the plot of logodds versus `gest3` is remarkably close to linear, and the assumption
of a log-linear relationship between the odds of low birth weight and gestation period
is a reasonable one. To find the effect of `gestwks` based on this assumption, try

. db effects

and press R. Then enter `lowbw` as *Response*, and select binary as *Type*. Enter `gestwks`
as *Exposure* and check the *Metric exposure* box. Select the *Measures of effect* tab and
check *Odds ratio*. Press *OK* to produce

. effects, res(lowbw) typ(binary) exp(gestwks) exm or

The effect of a unit increase in `gestwks` is to multiply the odds that the baby has low
birth weight by 0.408, i.e. a reduction to 41% of its current level for each extra week
of gestation.

We shall now return to the diet data and find the effect of `energy` on the rate
of CHD, where `energy` is a metric exposure variable, and the effect is measured as
a rate ratio per unit of energy. As before we assume that this effect is the same

---

[2] We have omitted 5 babies with less than 30 weeks gestation to avoid groups in which the odds
of low birth weight are infinite, so `gest3` has 3 categories.

throughout the range, that is the effect of changing from 1700 to 1701 kcal is the same as changing from 1702 to 1703, and so on throughout the range. This is the same as saying that the relationship between the log rate and **energy** is linear. First we check this assumption by cutting energy into equally spaced groups[3], and looking at how the rates change from one level to the next:

```
. use diet, clear
. egen eng4=cut(energy),at(1500(500)3500)
. tabmore, res(chd) typ(failure) row(eng4) rate fup(y) graph log
```

The plot looks reasonably close to linear, so try

```
. db effects
```

and press R. Then enter **chd** as *Response variable*, select failure as *Type*, and enter y as *Follow-up time*. Enter **energy** as *Exposure*, and check the *Metric exposure* box. Select the *Measures of effect* tab and check *Rate ratio*. Press *OK* to produce

```
. effects, res(chd) typ(failure) exp(energy) exm rr fup(y)
```

The effect of a unit increase in **energy** is 0.999, i.e. the CHD rate is reduced by a factor of 0.999 for each increase of 1 kcal in total energy. An increase of 1 kcal is a very small amount of energy, which explains why the effect is so close to 1. It would be better to measure the effect per 100 kcal, or even per 500 kcal. Recall the dialog box by typing **db effects** and then change *per unit* (bottom of the Main dialog box, opposite *Metric*) to 100. The effect is now 0.8913 per 100 kcal.

---

[3]The cut is chosen to omit 16 men whose energy intake is above 3500, thus avoiding a group with zero rate.

Exercises

1. Load the births data set and create the variable `agegrp` with

   ```
   . use births, clear
   . egen agegrp=cut(matage), at(20,30,35,40,45)
   ```

   Using `effects`, find the effects of `agegrp` on `bweight` as differences in means.

2. Repeat the previous question, changing the baseline to level 4.

3. Use `twoway scatter` to check whether birth weight changes linearly with maternal age.

4. Use `effects` to find the effect of `matage` on `bweight`, per year of maternal age.

5. Find the effects of `agegrp` on `preterm` using odds ratios.

6. Use `tabmore` to check on log linearity between `lowbw` and `agegrp`.

7. Use `effects` to find the effect of `matage` on `lowbw`, per year of maternal age.

Chapter 12

Stratifying and controlling

In this chapter we show how to control for potentially confounding variables by stratifying, estimating the effect(s) of an exposure within strata, and then combining the separate estimates.

12.1   Stratification

The effects calculated so far are *overall* (or crude) effects, and take no account of the possibility of confounding due to other variables. For example, in the births data, the overall effect of `hyp` on birth weight is -430.7 g, but the sex of the baby is associated with its birth weight, so if sex is also associated with hypertension, then part of the overall effect could be due to sex differences in the babies of normal and hypertensive women. To exclude this possibility we need to *stratify* the effect of `hyp` for `sex` by selecting `sex` as a stratifying variable. Start with

```
. use births, clear
. db effects
```

and press R. Then enter `bweight` as *Response* and select metric as *Type*. Enter `sex` as the *Stratifying variable*. Enter `hyp` as *Exposure*, select the *Measure of effect* tab, check *Difference in means*, and press *OK* to produce

```
. effects, res(bweight) typ(metric) exp(hyp) str(sex) exc md
Level of sex        Effect     95% Confidence Interval

1                   -496.35    [  -696.1 ,  -296.6 ]
2                   -379.77    [  -617.4 ,  -142.2 ]

Overall test for effect modification
chi2( 1)      =    0.542
```

```
P-value       =    0.462
```

The effect of `hyp` is -496.3 g for boys and -379.8 g for girls, and no part of these stratified effects can be due to sex differences between the babies of hypertensive and normal women, because the first is based only on boys, and the second only on girls. The p-value refers to the test of the null hypothesis that these two stratified effects are equal, i.e. that the difference between the two effects is zero. It has one degree of freedom because one difference is being tested.

12.2   Controlling

These separate estimates are each based on a subset of the data and have lower precision than the estimate based on the total data, but because there is no evidence that the true values of these two effects differ, they can be combined to give a single effect, -448.08 g, based on all of the data. The way they are combined need not concern us here, but is described in Chapters 13 and 15. This combined effect is called the effect of `hyp` controlled for `sex`. To see how to control the effect of `hyp` for `sex` start with

```
. db effects
```

but don't press R. Then remove `sex` as the *Stratifying variable*, select the *Control variables* tab, and enter `sex` as a *Categorical control variable*. Press *OK* to produce

```
. effects, res(bweight) typ(metric) exp(hyp) catcon(sex) exc md
```

The result should now look like this

```
Effect(s) of hyp

Levels       Effect    95% Confidence Interval
2/1          -448.08    [  -600.9 ,   -295.3 ]


Test for no effects
chi2(  1)    =   33.030
P-value      =    0.000
```

The effect of `hyp` controlled for `sex` is -448.08 g, and the p-value refers to the test of the null hypothesis that the effect of `hyp` controlled for `sex` is zero.

Although many people control for a potential confounder without first looking at the separate effects at different levels of the confounder, it is better to look first, because the separate effects are combined on the assumption that their true values are the same. The statistical test used to check this assumption is called the test for *effect modification*. When there is strong effect modification the separate effect of exposure should be reported.

As another example, we shall return to the diet data, and control the effect of hieng on the rate of CHD for job, first looking at the separate effects of hieng in the different jobs. Start by finding the overall effect of hieng (level 2 vs level 1) on chd, as a rate ratio, with

```
. use diet, clear
. db effects
```

Press R, then use the dialog box to produce

```
. effects, res(chd) typ(failure) exp(hieng) exc rr fup(y)
```

The effect of hieng should be 0.520. Now go back to db effects, select job as the *Stratifying variable*, and press *OK* to produce

```
. effects, res(chd) typ(failure) exp(hieng) str(job) exc rr fup(y)
```

You will now see three effects of hieng, one for each level of job:

```
Level of job      Effect    95% Confidence Interval

driver            0.410     [ 0.124 , 1.362 ]
conductor         0.655     [ 0.227 , 1.888 ]
bank              0.518     [ 0.212 , 1.267 ]


Overall test for effect modification
chi2( 2)      =    0.331
P-value       =    0.847
```

All three effects are measuring the effect of hieng, but in subjects who have different jobs. These three effects are similar in size, so there is no evidence that job modifies the size of the effect of hieng. This is confirmed by the significance test for effect modification which appears below the table. The chi–squared statistic is on 2 df because we are making two comparisons: 0.655 (conductors) with 0.410 (driver) and 0.518 (bank) with 0.410 (driver). The p-value is large, confirming that there is no evidence that job modifies the size of the effect of hieng.

We can now combine the three separate effects as a single effect, by removing job from being a stratifying variable in the *Main* tab, and selecting job as a control variable in the *Control variables* tab. Try this now – you should get 0.525 for the effect of hieng controlled for job, not very different from the overall, or uncontrolled effect of 0.520, showing that the confounding influence of job, if any, is minimal.

It is also possible to control for one variable while stratifying by another. For example, try

```
. db effects
```

but don't press R. Then increase the *Max number of values a categorical control variable can take* to 12. Select the *Control variables* tab and enter `month` as a *Categorical control variable*. Press *OK* to produce

```
. effects, res(chd) typ(failure) exp(hieng) str(job) exc catcon(month)
        maxval(12) rr fup(y)
```

The output shows the effect of `hieng`, controlled for month, but separately by job. Any number of control variables can be selected with `db effects`, but there can be only one stratifying variable.

12.3 Controlling the effect of a metric exposure

The effect of a metric exposure variable can be controlled for a confounding variable, in the same way as for a categorical exposure. For example, try

```
. db effects
```

and press R. Then enter `energy` as *Exposure* and check *Metric exposure*. Enter 100 in the *Per unit* box. Enter `job` as the *Stratifying variable*, select the *Measure of effect* tab, and check *Rate ratio*. Press *OK* to produce

```
. effects, res(chd) typ(failure) exp(energy) str(job) exm peru(100) rr fup(y)
```

The three effects you will see are the effects of energy per 100 kcal at each of the levels of `job`. They seem similar, and this is confirmed by the test for effect modification. Combine them by moving `job` from being a stratifying variable to being a control variable, to get 0.892 as the effect of `energy` per 100 kcal, controlled for `job`.

12.4 Metric control variables

To complete the story we need to discuss metric control variables. For example, suppose we want to control the effect of `hieng` on `chd` for `height`. On the assumption that the log rate changes linearly with `height`, this is easily done. Start with

```
. db effects
```

and press R. Then enter `chd` as *Response*, select *failure* as *Type*, and enter `y` as *Follow-up time*. Enter `hieng` as *Exposure*, select the *Measures of effect* tab and check *Rate ratio*. Select the *Control variables* tab and enter `height` as a *Metric control variable*. Press *OK* to produce

```
. effects, res(chd) typ(failure) exp(hieng) exc metcon(height) rr fup(y)
```

The effect of `hieng` controlled for `height` (metric) is 0.613. Of course, before doing this, you should check the linear relationship between the log rate and `height` by grouping `height`, and making a table of rates by grouped height, as follows:

```
. egen htgrp=cut(height),at(150(5)180)
. tabmore, res(chd) typ(failure) row(htgrp) rate fup(y) graph log
```

You will see that the assumption of a linear relationship between the log rate and `height` is not unreasonable.

12.5 Metric versus grouped

For a metric control variable, the issue is whether to control the effects of an exposure using the control variable in its metric form, or whether to group its values and control for it in a categorical form. Very similar results are usually obtained both ways, so this is a less important decision than how to measure the effects of an exposure (metric or categorical) in the first place. In general, when you have lots of data, group the control variable; when you have only a small amount of data, treat the control variable as metric.

When stratifying in order to check for effect modification, there is a strong case for treating the exposure as metric whenever possible. This is because with a metric exposure there will only be one effect per stratum, but when an exposure is grouped with, say, 5 levels there will 4 effects per stratum. Since there is usually only a small amount of data with which to estimate effects in each stratum, the fewer effects to estimate the better.

Exercises

1. Load the births data and find the effect of `hyp` on `preterm` using odds ratios.

2. Is this effect modified by `sex`? If not, find the effect per controlled for `sex`.

3. Find the effect per year of `matage` on `preterm` using odds ratios.

4. Is this effect modified by `sex`? If not, find the effect per year of `matage` controlled for `sex`.

5. Load the mortality data and find the effect of `nation` on the death rate as a rate ratio.

6. Is this effect modified by `agegrp`?

Chapter 13

Regression commands

The command **effects**, introduced in Chapter 11, is a convenient way of working, particularly when starting, but for more advanced analyses it is necessary to access the regression commands on which it depends. This chapter covers

- The **regress** command for a metric response.

- The **logit**, **logistic**, and **binreg** commands for a binary response.

- The **poisson** command for survival data.

- The **clogit** command for matched case-control studies.

These commands can all be found under the *Statistics* tab.

13.1 Three important regression models

The original (ordinary) regression model is

$$\mu = \alpha + \beta X$$

where μ is the mean of a metric response and X is an exposure. Later this was extended to the logistic regression model for a binary response

$$\ln\left(\frac{\pi}{1 - \pi}\right) = \alpha + \beta X$$

where π and $1 - \pi$ are the probabilities of the two possible responses. The third important model is Poisson regression for a failure or count response

$$\ln(\lambda) = \alpha + \beta X$$

where λ is the rate at which failures or events occur. In each case the variable X is a metric exposure variable, and α is the baseline corresponding to $X = 0$. The parameter β is the effect of a unit change in X on the mean (ordinary regression), or the log odds (logistic regression) or the log rate (Poisson regression).

Although the variable X is always metric in the basic regression model, there is a simple way of extending the basic model to cover categorical exposures. We shall now give examples of the use of each of the main regression models, starting with a metric exposure, followed by a categorical exposure with four levels.

13.2 A metric exposure

As an example of a metric exposure we shall find the effect of gestation period on birth weight using ordinary regression. The assumption of a constant effect of exposure throughout the range implies a linear relationship between mean birth weight and gestation period of the form

$$\text{Mean birth weight} = \alpha + \beta(X - 24)$$

where for convenience the gestation period (X) has been measured from 24 weeks. Graphically the model looks like this:

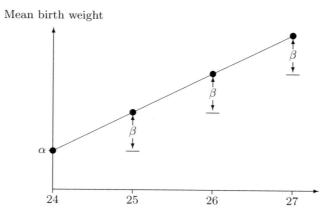

The parameter α is the mean birth weight at 24 weeks, and β is the increase in the mean birth weight for each unit increase in gestation period. To estimate the values of α and β using Stata, try

```
. use births, clear
. generate gestwks24=gestwks-24
. regress bweight gestwks24
```

Note that the response bweight comes immediately after the command, and is followed by the exposure variable gestwks24. The important part of the output is shown below. [1]

```
    bweight |     Coef.    [95% Conf. Interval]
------------+-----------------------------------
  gestwks24 |   196.9726    179.7054    214.2399
      _cons |   238.2033   -19.11787    495.5244
```

which shows that β is 197 g, with confidence interval from 180 to 214 g. The _cons term is 238, and this is the value of α, the baseline birth weight at 24 weeks. If the gestation period had been measured from 0 rather than 24 weeks, α would have been the result of extrapolating the line back to 0 weeks. Try

```
. regress bweight gestwks
```

and you will see that the _cons term is now -4489, although β is unchanged.

With lowbw as response the regression model is

$$\text{log odds of low birth weight} = \alpha + \beta(X - 24)$$

where α is the log of the baseline odds and β is the change in the log odds of being low birth weight for an increase of 1 week in gestation. To estimate the values of α and β using Stata, try

```
. logit lowbw gestwks24
```

The value of α is 10.3326, and the value of β is -0.8965. The exponential of -0.8965 is 0.408 which is the odds ratio for each additonal week of gestation. To get this directly, try

```
. logit lowbw gestwks24, or
```

The effect of gestwks (or gestwks24) is a reduction in the odds of being low birth weight by a factor of 0.408 for every extra week of gestation. The value next to _cons is the baseline odds, i.e. the odds of low birth weight in babies born at 24 weeks.

To demonstrate the Poisson regression model we shall find the effect of energy on the rate of CHD in the diet data set. The regression model is

$$\ln(\lambda) = \alpha + \beta X$$

---

[1]The first half of the output, headed Source, describes the partition of the total variability in the data between that explained by the regression model and what is left (the residual). In most applications this is of little interest.

where λ is the rate of CHD and X refers to the variable **energy**. The parameter β is the change in log rate for an increase of 1 unit in X, i.e. 1 kcal. The parameter α is the baseline log rate when the energy intake is zero. To estimate the values of α and β try

```
. use diet, clear
. poisson chd energy, e(y)
```

Note that the follow-up time is given in the option **e(y)**. The value of β is -0.0011507 and the exponential of this is 0.9988. You can get this directly with

```
. poisson chd energy, e(y) irr
```

where the option **irr** asks for incidence rate ratios (i.e. rate ratios). As with **logit**, when the exponentiated form of the output is produced, the value next to **_cons** is the baseline rate corresponding to a 0 kcal diet.

To get the effect of energy per 100 kcal (say), try

```
. generate energy100=energy/100
. poisson chd energy100, e(y) irr
```

The effect is now a reduction in the rate of CHD by a factor of 0.8913 per 100 kcals increase in energy. The baseline rate obviously does not change.

The commands **regress, logit, poisson** are examples of **estimation** commands. In the same way that most Stata commands leave information behind in the **return list**, so estimation commands leave information behind also in the **ereturn list**. To see what is left by the previous **poisson** command, type **ereturn list**.

13.3   Categorical exposures

Suppose that X refers to a categorical exposure with 3 levels, coded 1,2,3. Changing from level 1 to level 2 is a unit change in X, as is changing from level 2 to level 3, but there is no reason to assume that the effects of these two changes are the same. The model

$$\alpha + \beta X$$

is no longer appropriate because it insists that all unit changes in X have the same effect. Instead X is replaced by *indicator variables*, defined in the table below.

Exposure level	X_1	X_2	X_3
1	1	0	0
2	0	1	0
3	0	0	1

X_1 indicates level 1 by taking the value 1 for subjects whose exposure is at level 1, and 0 for all others. Similarly for X_2 and X_3. Replacing X by its indicators, the right-hand side of the regression model is now

$$\alpha + \beta_1 X_1 + \beta_2 X_2 + \beta_3 X_3$$

To make the baseline for the effects equal to level 1 of the exposure, the variable X_1 is removed from the model to give

$$\alpha + \beta_2 X_2 + \beta_3 X_3$$

Substituting the values of the indicator variables for the three levels of exposure gives

$$\begin{array}{ll} \alpha & \text{for level 1} \\ \alpha + \beta_2 & \text{for level 2} \\ \alpha + \beta_3 & \text{for level 3} \end{array}$$

which shows that β_2 is the effect of exposure (level 2 vs level 1) and β_3 is the effect (level 3 vs level 1).

In Stata categorical variables are called *factors* and all this is done automatically by the i. prefix which declares that a particular variable is a factor. Note that factors must be coded with non-negative integers. To demonstrate we shall cut gestwks into gest4 with 4 categories coded 20, 35, 37, 39. The notation i.gest4 causes Stata to create four indicator variables indicating the category to which each subject belongs. You can see this with

```
. use births, clear
. egen gest4=cut(gestwks), at(20,35,37,39,45)
. sort gest4
. list gest4 i.gest4
```

Scrolling down the output, subjects in the first category are coded 0 for all four indicators, subjects in the second category are coded 1 for the second indicator but 0 for the others, and so on (use the *Break* icon when you want to stop the listing). The indicators are *virtual variables*, and are named with the codes for the different categories. They are not added to the data (so you cannot see them if you browse), but are created afresh every time a command refers to i.gest4. To fit the model showing how bweight changes with the level of gest4, try

```
. regress bweight i.gest4
```

The relevant bit of the output is

```
    bweight |      Coef.    [95% Conf. Interval]
------------+----------------------------------
      gest4 |
         35 |   856.5706    619.6882    1093.453
         37 |   1360.025    1176.197    1543.853
         39 |    1667.52    1488.913    1846.126
            |
      _cons |   1733.742    1564.917    1902.567
```

The _cons term is the birth weight when all the indicators are zero, i.e. the birth weight corresponding to the first level of gest4. The lines in the output under gest4 refer to the indicator variables 35.gest4, 37.gest4, and 39.gest4 and the coefficients of these variables are the three effects of gest4 using the first level as the baseline. Thus the effect of level 2 vs level 1 is 856.57, and so on. These results can be checked using the table of mean birth weight by gest4:

. table gest4, c(mean bweight)

```
    gest4 | mean(bweight)
----------+--------------
       20 |      1733.74
       35 |      2590.31
       37 |      3093.77
       39 |      3401.26
```

In the regression model the first level of gest4 is the baseline by default. The second level is coded 35, and to make this the baseline try

. regress bweight b35.gest4

or , equivalently

. regress bweight b(#2).gest4

where b(#2).gest4 sets the baseline for gest4 to be the second level. To make the last level of gest4 the baseline try

. regress bweight b(last).gest4

Finally note that including b35.gest4 in a command changes the baseline for that command only, but the level can be changed permanently with fvset as in

. fvset base 35 gest4
. list gest4 i.gest4

111

13.4 Ratios of odds, proportions, and rates

To compare the odds of the baby being low birth weight by the level of `gest4` try

```
. fvset base 20 gest4
. logit lowbw i.gest4, or
```

The output from `logit` with the option `or` shows odds ratios comparing the odds of the baby being low birth weight for each level of gestational age compared to the first. The effect of changing from the first to the second level is to decrease the odds by a factor of 0.164; from the first to the third the odds are reduced by a factor of 0.029, and from the first to the fourth by a factor of 0.003. To see why the results are in terms of odds ratios, first make a table of the odds by level of `gest4` with `tabmore`:

```
Summary using odds per 1
----------------------
    gest4 |   response
----------+-----------
       20 |      4.17
       35 |      0.68
       37 |      0.12
       39 |      0.01
```

Because the model relates the log odds to the level of `gest4` the effect of level 2 versus level 1 of `gest4` is

$$\ln(0.68) - \ln(4.17) = \ln(0.68/4.17)$$

i.e. the log odds ratio. The command `logistic` does the same as `logit` but automatically gives the answers as odds ratios.

The related command `binreg` can be used to calculate effects as ratios of proportions, or differences between proportions. For example, to use the ratio of proportions (risk) instead of odds, try

```
. binreg lowbw i.gest4, rr
```

where the option `rr` stands for *risk ratio*. To use the difference between proportions, try

```
. binreg lowbw i.gest4, rd
```

where `rd` stands for *risk difference*. The `binreg` command can also be used for odds ratios by using the option `or` – the results should be the same as with `logit, or`.

For survival time data, when effects are measured as rate ratios, the `poisson` command is used. To find the effect of `hieng` as a rate ratio, using the diet data set, try

```
. use diet, clear
. poisson chd i.hieng, e(y) irr
```

13.5   Fitted values and residuals

Following any regression command it is possible to predict the response for each subject, using the regression model. These predictions are called fitted values. The difference between the fitted values and the observed values are called the residuals, and these can be useful when checking on how well a regression model fits the data. For the births data, try

```
. use births, clear
. regress bweight gestwks
. predict bwpred
```

which places the fitted values from the regression of `bweight` on `gestwks` in the new variable `bwpred`. The `predict` command picks up the results left behind by `regress` to do this, and any name can be used for the new variable which contains the predictions. A plot of the fitted line is obtained with

```
. twoway line bwpred gestwks, sort
```

Similarly

```
. predict bwres, residuals
```

places the residuals from the regression of `bweight` on `gestwks` in the new variable `bwres`. A histogram of the residuals is obtained with

```
. histogram bwres
```

which is roughly normal in shape.

When following `logit` with `predict` there is a choice of saving a variable holding the predicted probability of low birth weight babies (the default) or the predicted log of the odds for being low birth weight. The latter is found with the option `xb`. Plotting it against `gestwks` shows that the predicted log odds are linearly related to the explanatory variable.

```
. logit lowbw gestwks
. predict lpred, xb
. twoway line lpred gestwks, sort
```

On the probability scale the plot of the predicted probabilities against `gestwks` shows a curved relationship:

```
. predict ppred
. twoway line ppred gestwks, sort
```

Pearson residuals can be obtained with

```
. predict pres, residuals
```

13.6 Case-control studies

Unmatched case-control studies can be analysed prospectively with `logit` (or `logistic`) using as response the variable which records whether or not the subject is a case. For example, try

```
. use guy, clear
. expand N
. drop N
. logit d i.activity, or
```

to see the three effects of `activity` as odds ratios relative to the lowest level of activity.

Group matched case-control studies, where the matching has been on variables such as age and sex, can also be analysed using logistic regression, but it is still necessary to control for the matching variables, even though, as a result of matching, they are not associated with the disease outcome (case/control). Failure to do this results in a biased estimate of the effect of exposure. This is a consequence of using odds, and cannot be avoided with case-control studies. To illustrate the point, consider the made-up data in Table 13.1. There are 100 cases and 100 controls in each stratum, so the disease outcome is independent of strata. The odds ratio in each stratum is close to 2.0, so intuitively, because the disease outcome is independent of strata, we would expect the odds ratio when strata are ignored also to be 2.0. The fact that it is 1.7 is entirely due to the fact that we are using odds ratios.

Table 13.1: Bias due to ignoring matching

	Cases		Controls		Odds
Stratum	Exposed	Unexposed	Exposed	Unexposed	ratio
1	89	11	80	20	2.02
2	67	33	50	50	2.03
3	33	67	20	80	1.97
Total	189	111	150	150	1.70

For individually matched studies, where the data consist of matched sets containing a case and one or more matched controls, the requirement that the analysis controls for the matched sets means that logistic regression cannot be used, because there would be one parameter for each set which would be too many. Collecting more data does not help because every new matched sets adds a new parameter. Instead it is necessary to use conditional logistic regression.

To illustrate the analysis of individually matched case-control studies we shall use data from a study of an outbreak of salmonellosis in Denmark[10]. Cases and two agesex- and residency-matched controls were telephone interviewed and asked whether they had travelled abroad, or eaten any of a list of foods, in the previous two weeks. The list included beef, pork, veal, poultry, liverpaste, vegetables, fruit, and eggs. The participants were also asked at which retailer(s) they had purchased meat, and independently of this, retailers were linked to meat processing plants. The participants were thus linked to plants, and the results for plant7 are of interest here. The data are in the file `salmonella.dta`: the variable `case` identifies cases and controls, and the variable `set` identifies the matched sets. All questions are coded 1 for yes, 0 for no.

We shall first attempt to find the effect of `plant7` after controlling for the matching using logistic regression, Try

```
. use salmonella, clear
. logistic case i.plant7 i.set
```

You will first see the effect of `plant7`, which is 10.48, and then many effects of `set`. Because of the large number of parameters and the small amount of data in each stratum, we cannot rely on this result.

Conditioning on the total number of exposed subjects in each set gives a likelihood which depends only on the common odds ratio, so using this conditional likelihood avoids the problem of too many parameters. The `clogit` command, uses the conditional likelihood:

```
. clogit case i.plant7, group(set) or
```

Here the response is `case`, the exposure is `plant7`, and the variable which identifies the matched sets is `set`. Now the effect of `plant7` is 4.47, very different from the 10.48 obtained with logistic regression.

One occasion where matching is often ignored in a logistic regression is with *incidence density sampling* where cases are selected over time and controls are then matched to cases on time. Here time is a matching variable, so it would seem that we should include it in the analysis using conditional logistic regression, but in fact it can be ignored, provided the exposure does not change with time. This is because time is unrelated to both outcome and exposure, and this is the one situation where ignoring a matching variable does not bias the odds ratio for exposure.

Exercises

1. Load the births data and create the categorical variable `mage4` from `matage` so that it has 4 similarly sized groups. Use `table` (or `tabmore`) to find the mean birth weight of babies born to mothers in these age groups.

2. Find the effects of `mage4` on birth weight, with confidence intervals.

3. Repeat the previous question using the metric variable `matage` and find the effect per year of `matage` on birth weight.

4. Find the effects of `mage4` on the odds of a baby having low birth weight.

5. Repeat the previous question using the metric variable `matage` and find the effect of `matage` per 10 years.

Chapter 14

Tests of hypotheses

In this chapter we introduce the likelihood ratio test and its quadratic approximation, the Wald test. The Stata commands are `lrtest` and `testparm`.

14.1 Models and Likelihood

The fundamental statistical test is the likelihood ratio test. To understand this requires a knowledge of likelihood, and this in turn requires a knowledge of probability models. Some readers might find these concepts unfamiliar, so we shall make a detour from the main business of the book, and give a very brief description of them in this section.

Consider a binary response with two outcomes, A and B, and suppose that the observations were

A A B A B B B A B B

i.e. 4 A's and 6 B's. As it stands this statement has no scientific interest, because it refers only to the 10 subjects studied. To be of scientific interest it must be generalized to some population of subjects, for example the population of all subjects who could have been in the study. We also need a further assumption, namely that the data arose from the population by a random mechanism. The most common mechanism is random sampling, which is a special case of the binary probability model in which, for each subject, outcome A occurs with probability π and outcome B occurs with probability $1 - \pi$. The probability π is called the parameter of the model, and is the same for all subjects. In the case of random sampling π is the true proportion of subjects with outcome A in the population from which the sample was drawn. Based on the 10 subjects in the study, the estimated value of π is $4/10 = 0.4$.

Loosely speaking likelihood is the probability of the observed data given the probability model which gave rise to these data. It is used to compare different possible

117

values for the parameter of the model. In this case the likelihood is

$$
\begin{aligned}
L(\pi) &= \pi \times \pi \times (1-\pi) \times \pi \times (1-\pi) \times (1-\pi) \times (1-\pi) \times \pi \times (1-\pi) \times (1-\pi) \\
&= \pi^4 (1-\pi)^6
\end{aligned}
$$

and this expression is used to calculate the likelihood for different values of π. For example, the likelihood for $\pi = 0.2$ is

$$
L(0.2) = (0.2)^4 \times (0.8)^6 = 41.94 \times 10^{-5}
$$

and the likelihood for $\pi = 0.4$ is

$$
L = (0.4)^4 \times (0.6)^6 = 119.44 \times 10^{-5}
$$

From this we can say that the data are more likely if $\pi = 0.4$ than if $\pi = 0.2$. In this example the data are more likely if $\pi = 0.4$ than for any other value of π, so it makes sense to use $\pi = 0.4$ as the value *most likely* to have given rise to the data.

To test whether $\pi = 0.2$ could have given rise to the data the likelihood for $\pi = 0.2$ is compared to the likelihood for $\pi = 0.4$ (the most likely value) using the likelihood ratio

$$
L(0.2)/L(0.4) = 41.94/119.44 = 0.3512
$$

The p-value for $\pi = 0.2$ is the probability of observing a likelihood ratio less 0.3512; if the p-value is low then $\pi = 0.2$ is very unlikely to have given rise to the data. The p-value can be found using a central result in statistics which in this case states that in repeated samples from the model with $\pi = 0.2$, minus twice the natural logarithm of the likelihood ratio has (approximately) a chi-squared distribution on 1 df. The p-value is therefore the same as the probability of observing a value greater than

$$
-2 \times \ln(0.3512) = 2.0930
$$

in a chi-squared distribution on 1 df. The Stata command

```
. display chi2tail(1,2.0930)
0.14797
```

shows that this probability is 0.148, so there is no evidence against $\pi = 0.2$ having given rise to the data, as opposed to $\pi = 0.4$, the most likely value. This test is called the likelihood ratio (LR) test.

To see whether $\pi = 0.1$ could have given rise to the data, we calculate the likelihood for $\pi = 0.1$, which is

$$
L(0.1) = 0.1^4 \times 0.9^6 = 5.31 \times 10^{-5}
$$

and obtain the likelihood ratio

$$
L(0.1)/L(0.4) = 5.31/119.44 = 0.0445
$$

Minus twice the log likelihood ratio is

$$-2 \times \ln(0.0445) = -2 \times -3.1124 = 6.2245$$

and

```
. display chi2tail(1,6.2245)
0.0126
```

shows that the p-value is 0.0126. Thus the evidence against $\pi = 0.1$ having given rise to the data is quite strong.

14.2   Log likelihood

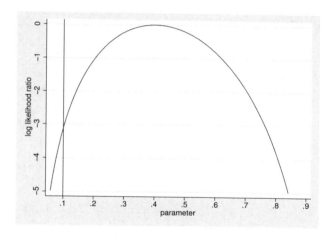

Figure 14.1: Plot of log likelihood ratio against the probability parameter

A more convenient way of looking at a likelihood ratio is to look at the difference in log likelihoods. Writing LL for log likelihood

$$
\begin{array}{llll}
L(0.1) & = & 5.31 \times 10^{-5}, & LL(0.1) & = & -9.8425 \\
L(0.4) & = & 119.44 \times 10^{-5}, & LL(0.4) & = & -6.7301
\end{array}
$$

The LLR comparing $\pi = 0.1$ with $\pi = 0.4$ is the difference between the log likelihoods,

$$LLR(0.1) = LL(0.1) - LL(0.4) = -9.8425 - (-6.7301) = -3.1123.$$

Figure 14.1 shows a plot of the log likelihood ratio (LLR) comparing different values of π with the most likely value 0.4. The LLR peaks at $\pi = 0.4$ taking the value zero, and

119

drops to -3.11 when $\pi = 0.1$. If the LLR is plotted against the logodds parameter, the resulting curve is usually a bit closer to a quadratic shape (upside down pudding bowl) – see Figure 14.2. A quadratic approximation to the LLR curve plotted against the logodds parameter is shown in Figure 14.3. The drop in the approximate LLR at $\pi = 0.1$, (logodds equal to $\ln(0.1/0.9) = -2.20$), is -3.80, and the corresponding p-value for $\pi = 0.1$ is found from the probability of values above $-2 \times -3.80 = 7.60$ in a chi-squared distribution on 1 df. When the quadratic approximation is used for the drop in LLR the test is called a Wald test.

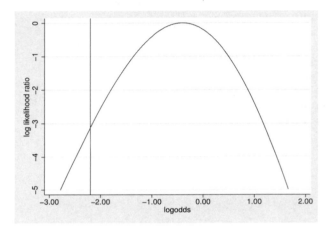

Figure 14.2: Plot of log likelihood against the log odds parameter

14.3 Likelihood ratio and Wald tests in Stata

In practice statistical tests are usually about special values of a parameter which correspond to nothing going on - the so-called null values. For example, if the parameter is an odds ratio then the null value is 1; if it is the log odds ratio, then the null value is the log of 1 which is 0. As an example we shall test whether the odds ratio measuring the effect of maternal hypertension on low birth weight is 1. The effect of **hyp** on a log scale is found with

```
. use births, clear
. logit lowbw i.hyp
lowbw |      Coef.   [95% Conf. Interval]
------+-------------------------------------------------------------
1.hyp |   1.316614    .7067913     1.926438
_cons |  -2.272126   -2.597606    -1.946646
```

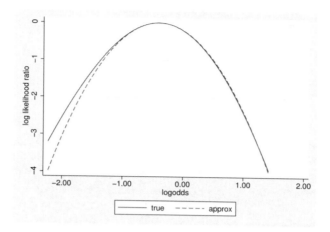

Figure 14.3: Quadratic approximation to the plot of log likelihood against the log odds parameter

so the most likely value of the odds ratio parameter is $\exp(1.3166) = 3.73$. The log likelihood, reported by `logit`, is -175.42. To test the null value of 1 (0 for the log odds ratio) we need to see how much lower the log likelihood is when the parameter takes its null value. This is found by leaving out `hyp` as in

```
. logit lowbw
lowbw |     Coef.    [95% Conf. Interval]
------+--------------------------------
_cons |   -1.99243   -2.262161   -1.722699
```

which reports a log likelihood of -183.46. The drop in log likelihood is therefore

$$-183.46 + 175.42 = -8.04$$

and minus twice this is 16.08. The probability of exceeding 16.08 in a chi-squared distribution on 1 df is found from

```
. display chi2tail(1,16.08)
0.00006
```

so the evidence against a log odds ratio of 0 (odds ratio of 1) having given rise to these data is very strong. All this can be automated using the `lrtest` command:

```
. logit lowbw i.hyp
. estimates store tmp
. logit lowbw if e(sample)
. lrtest tmp
likelihood-ratio test              LR chi2(1)   =      16.08
(Assumption: . nested in tmp) Prob > chi2  =     0.0001
```

which fits the model including i.hyp, stores the results in tmp (or whatever name you choose), refits leaving out i.hyp and finally carries out the likelihood ratio test. The last line of the Stata output reminds you that the second model fitted must be obtained from the first by setting some parameters to their null values, i.e. by leaving some variables out. This causes problems when there are missing values in the variables being left out because this will result in there being fewer observations in the first model than the second. The use of if e(sample) in the second model makes sure that the same observations are used in both models. In this case there are no missing values in hyp so the use of if e(sample) is not necessary, but it is good to get in the habit of using it.

The Wald test is rather easier to carry out as the model needs to be fitted only once. The command is testparm. Try

```
. logit lowbw i.hyp
. testparm i.hyp
 ( 1)   [lowbw]1.hyp = 0

        chi2(  1) =    17.91
      Prob > chi2 =     0.0000
```

The command testparm i.hyp asks for a test that the parameters associated with the virtual variables i.hyp are zero. In this case there is only one virtual variable. The chi-squared of 17.91 is close to the value 16.08 obtained with the LR test. The difference is due to the fact that a quadratic approximation has been used for the LLR in the Wald test. Both tests can be used with logistic in place of logit.

14.4 Joint tests of several parameters

For a categorical exposure on (say) four levels, there are three effects, and it rarely makes sense to test each effect separately. Instead the three null values are tested jointly with a chi-squared on three df. As an example we shall consider whether low birth weight depends on maternal age. Start by cutting maternal age into four groups with

```
. egen agegrp=cut(matage), at(20,30,35,40,45)
. tabulate agegrp
```

and try

```
. logit lowbw i.agegrp, or
. estimates store tmp
. logit lowbw if e(sample), or
. lrtest tmp
likelihood-ratio test                LR chi2(3)  =        1.63
(Assumption: . nested in tmp)        Prob > chi2 =      0.6532
```

The test is a test of the null hypothesis that all three true effects are 1, or zero on a log scale. With a Wald test:

```
. logit lowbw i.agegrp, or
. testparm i.agegrp
 ( 1)   [lowbw]30.agegrp = 0
 ( 2)   [lowbw]35.agegrp = 0
 ( 3)   [lowbw]40.agegrp = 0

          chi2(  3) =      1.58
        Prob > chi2 =      0.6649
```

14.5   Other regression commands

Both the LR test and the Wald test can be used with any of the other regression commands. With **regress**, however, they give essentially the same result because the appropriate log likelihood is Gaussian and the quadratic approximation to this log likelihood is perfect. There is a very small difference in the output, as you will see in the following example. First the LR test:

```
. regress bweight i.hyp
. estimates store tmp
. regress bweight if e(sample)
. lrtest tmp


likelihood-ratio test                LR chi2(1)  =       29.02
(Assumption: . nested in tmp)        Prob > chi2 =      0.0000
```

then the Wald test:

```
. regress bweight i.hyp
. testparm i.hyp
 ( 1)   1.hyp = 0

        F(  1,    498) =     29.76
             Prob > F =      0.0000
```

The difference is that the Wald test takes account of the fact that the residual variability in the response is estimated from the data. For this reason it uses the F distribution to find the p-value. The two tests give almost the same answer provided the data set is not too small.

Exercises

1. Load the diet data and find the effect of **hieng** as a rate ratio using Poisson regression. Test whether this effect is significantly different from 1, using both a LR test and a Wald test.

2. Test whether the effect of **energy** per kcal is significantly different from 1, using both a LR test and a Wald test.

3. Load the births data and find the effect of **hyp** on **lowbw** as an odds ratio, using **logit**. Test whether this effect is significantly different from 1 using both a LR test and a Wald test.

Chapter 15

Controlling and stratifying with regression

This chapter shows how to use the regression commands to find the effects of one variable controlled for another, how to find the effects of one variable stratified by another, and how to test for effect modification using interactions.

15.1   Controlling with regression commands

Regression commands can have more than one explanatory variable. As an example we shall use the births data to study how `bweight` varies with both `gestwks`, which is metric, and `sex`, which is categorical. Try

```
. use births, clear
. regress bweight gestwks i.sex
```

The interpretation of the coefficients for `gestwks` and `2.sex` is as follows:

- The effect of a unit change in `gestwks` when `sex` is kept constant (i.e. when we control for `sex`) is an increase of 196 g of birth weight.

- The effect of a change in level of `sex` from male to female when `gestwks` is kept constant (i.e. when we control for `gestwks`) is a decrease of 189.9 g in birth weight.

We can also find the effect of `gestwks` controlled for `sex` using `effects`:

```
. effects, res(bweight) typ(metric) exp(gestwks) exm catcon(sex) md
```

The answer should be 196 g. Similarly, the effect of `sex` controlled for `gestwks` could be found by declaring `sex` as a categorical exposure and `gestwks` as a metric control variable. Try

```
. effects, res(bweight) typ(metric) exp(sex) exc metcon(gestwks) md
```

and you should get -189.9 g.

The `effects` command treats one variable as the exposure and the other as control and reports the effect of the exposure variable controlled for the control variable. Regression commands treat the two variables symmetrically, and report the effects of each variable controlled for the other. As another example we shall use `lowbw` as the response, and look at the effects of `gestwks` controlled for `sex` and the effects of `sex` controlled for `gestwks`. When effects are measured using odds ratios the appropriate command is

```
. logit lowbw gestwks i.sex, or
```

The effect of a unit increase in `gestwks`, controlling for `sex`, is to reduce the odds of low birth weight by a factor of 0.405, and the effect of a change in level `sex` from male to female, controlled for `gestwks`, is to increase the odds of low birth weight by a factor of 1.510.

15.2   Testing effects after controlling

This can be done using either the LR test or the Wald test. For example, to test the effect of `gestwks` on `lowbw` controlled for `sex` using the LR test, try

```
. logit lowbw gestwks i.sex
. estimates store tmp
. logit lowbw i.sex if e(sample)
. lrtest tmp
```

The first `logit` is based on 490 subjects because there are 10 missing values for `gestwks`. Without the `if e(sample)` the second `logit`, which does not use `gestwks`, would be based on 500 subjects, rendering the test invalid. Including the `if e(sample)` with the second `logit` makes sure it is based on the same subjects as the first. Note that it is the variable you want to test that is left out when fitting the second model - this is because you want to find out how much the log likelihood goes down when the parameter for that variable is set to its null value. To do the same thing with the Wald test, try

```
. logit lowbw gestwks i.sex
. testparm gestwks
```

15.3   Testing for effect modification

When the effects of an exposure vary between strata there is said to be effect modification. To see how to measure the extent of effect modification we shall use, as an example, the effects of hieng within job, and ask whether job modifies the effect of hieng. First we look at the effects of hieng within each job using effects:

```
. use diet, replace
. effects, res(chd) typ(failure) exp(hieng) str(job) exc rr fup(y)
```

```
Level of job    Effect    95% Confidence Interval
driver          0.410     [  0.12 ,   1.36 ]
conductor       0.655     [  0.23 ,   1.89 ]
bank            0.518     [  0.21 ,   1.27 ]
```

Because the three effects are rate ratios a natural way of comparing them is to take the ratios of the second and third against the first:

job	Effects of hieng level 2/1 Effect	Ratio
1	0.410	$0.410/0.410 = 1$
2	0.655	$0.655/0.410 = 1.597$
3	0.518	$0.518/0.410 = 1.262$

The two ratios 1.597 and 1.262 are called *interactions* between hieng and job. To produce the interactions using poisson, we need to create indicators for the interactions by multiplying the indicators for hieng by the indicators for job.

The variable hieng is coded 0,1. When it is included in a command with the prefix i. as in i.hieng, the virtual variables 0.hieng, 1.hieng are produced. Similarly for the variable job which is coded 1,2,3. When i.job is included in a Stata command the virtual variables 1.job, 2.job, 3.job are created. Products between these two sets of indicators are created using the operator #, pronounced *cross*. Try

```
. list i.hieng#i.job, nolabel
```

which shows that each indicator for hieng has been multiplied by each indicator for job to produce six new indicators as virtual variables. Now try

```
. poisson chd i.hieng i.job i.hieng#i.job, e(y) irr
```

Altogether this model contains $2 + 3 + 6 = 11$ indicators, but of these, the indicators for the baselines of hieng, job and the products between these baselines and the other indicators are automatically dropped. After running the poisson command you should see the following (abbreviated) table:

```
        chd |         IRR    [95% Conf. Interval]
------------+-----------------------------------
   1.hieng |    .4102648    .1235412   1.362438
            |
        job |
          2 |    1.136857    .4266828   3.029051
          3 |    .813427     .3325064   1.989927
            |
  hieng#job |
        1 2 |    1.596755    .3222813   7.911183
        1 3 |    1.261973    .2824452   5.638532
```

The fourth and fifth rows show the two interactions. The first three rows of the table refer to the effect of hieng at the first level of job, and the effects of job at the first level of hieng. These three effects are of little interest – only the interactions are useful. A slightly shorter way of writing the model uses the ## operator, pronounced *double cross*:

```
. poisson chd i.hieng##i.job, e(y) irr
```

The term i.hieng##i.job is equivalent to i.hieng i.job i.hieng#i.job.[1]

When the three effects of hieng at the different levels of job are the same (i.e. there is no effect modification) the interactions will both be 1, apart from random variation. The test for no effect modification is therefore the same as the test that the interaction parameters are 1 (or 0 on a log scale). Try

```
. testparm i.hieng#i.job
```

to test for interactions using a Wald test. You will see that the chi-squared statistic on 2 df is 0.33, and the p-value is 0.8475, so there is no evidence of effect modification.

To do the same thing with the LR test, try

```
. poisson chd i.hieng##i.job, e(y) irr
. estimates store tmp
. poisson chd i.hieng i.job, e(y) irr
. lrtest tmp
```

The second poisson command fits the model without the interaction terms. In this case the interactions between hieng and job do not differ significantly from 1, so we use the output from the second model (without interactions) to estimates the effect of hieng controlled for job.

```
. poisson chd i.hieng i.job, e(y) irr
```

---

[1]Help on factor variables can be obtained with help fvvarlist.

```
       chd |      IRR    [95% Conf. Interval]
-----------+----------------------------------
  1.hieng |   .5247666    .290225     .9488499
           |
       job |
         2 |  1.358442   .6282879    2.937133
         3 |  .8843023   .4322823    1.808981
```

The effect of `hieng` controlled for `job` is 0.525. The other two terms are the effects of `job` controlled for `hieng`.

15.4   Interactions with metric variables

To obtain interactions between a categorical variable and a metric variable the metric variable must be prefaced with `c.`, as in

```
. poisson chd c.height##i.hieng, e(y) irr
```

```
       chd |      IRR    [95% Conf. Interval]
-----------+----------------------------------
    height |   .9258995   .8796093    .9746259
  1.hieng |   99.00107   .0000106    9.25e+08
           |
    hieng#|
  c.height |
         1 |   .9706023   .8833194    1.06651
```

As before the effects in the first two rows are not useful – only the interaction is of interest. Note that the order with which variables are listed to create their interaction does not matter.

When both variables are metric both must be prefixed with `c.` as in

```
. gen energy100=energy/100
. poisson chd c.energy100##c.height, e(y) irr
```

The third row shows the interaction. The significance of this interaction is tested with

```
. testparm c.energy100#c.height
```

A special type of interaction is that of a continuous variable with itself, which is equivalent to creating a squared term for that variable. For example

```
. poisson chd height c.height#c.height, e(y) irr
```

fits a model with height and height squared as explanatory variables.

15.5 Stratifying with regression commands

The effect of `hieng` stratified by `job` was found earlier with

`. effects, res(chd) typ(failure) exp(hieng) exc str(job) rr fup(y)`

There are three effects of `hieng`, one for each level of `job`. To do the same thing with regression commands try

`. poisson chd i.job i.hieng#i.job, e(y) irr`

which produces the stratified effects. The equality of these effects can be tested with

`. testparm i.hieng#i.job, equal`

which gives the same answer as the test for interaction.

A natural question is why does this model give the stratified effects? Using H_0, H_1 to refer to the indicators for `hieng` and J_1, J_2, J_3 to refer to the indicators for `job` the right hand side of the model can be written

$$\alpha + \beta_1 J_1 + \beta_2 J_2 + \beta_3 J_3 + \beta_{01} H_0 J_1 + \beta_{02} H_0 J_2 + \beta_{03} H_0 J_3 + \beta_{11} H_1 J_1 + \beta_{12} H_1 J_2 + \beta_{13} H_1 J_3$$

Of these $\beta_1 J_1$ and terms involving H_0 are dropped leaving

$$\alpha + \beta_2 J_2 + \beta_3 J_3 + \beta_{11} H_1 J_1 + \beta_{12} H_1 J_2 + \beta_{13} H_1 J_3$$

When `job` is at level 1 and `hieng` is at level 0 we have $J_2 = 0, J_3 = 0, H_1 = 0$ so the right hand side of the model reduces to α. When `job` is at level 1 and `hieng` is at level 1 we have $J_2 = 0, J_3 = 0, H_1 = 1$ so the right hand side of the model reduces to $\alpha + \beta_{11}$. Coninuing in this way for all combinations of `hieng` and `job` we get:

	job		
hieng	1	2	3
0	α	$\alpha + \beta_2$	$\alpha + \beta_3$
1	$\alpha + \beta_{11}$	$\alpha + \beta_2 + \beta_{12}$	$\alpha + \beta_3 + \beta_{13}$

It follows that the effects of `hieng` within the levels of `job` are β_{11}, β_{12} and β_{13}.

15.6 Categorical variables in models before Stata 11

Before Stata 11 categorical variables in models were dealt with using the `xi:` command which is short for *expand indicators*. For example, instead of

`. poisson chd i.hieng i.job, e(y) irr`

earlier versions of Stata used

```
. xi: poisson chd i.hieng i.job, e(y) irr
```

You will see that the numerical results are the same but the naming of the indicator variables is much improved in Stata 11 and 12. Interactions were dealt with using the * operator, so instead of

```
. poisson chd i.hieng##i.job, e(y) irr
```

earlier versions of Stata used

```
. xi: poisson chd i.hieng*i.job, e(y) irr
```

The improvement in the naming of variables is even more apparent.

Exercises

1. Load the births data set and use `logistic` to find the effect of `hyp` on `preterm` as an odds ratio.

2. Cut `matage` into 2 groups with

   ```
   . egen mage2=cut(matage), at(20,40,45) label
   ```

   and use `logistic` with interactions to study whether `mage2` modifies the effect of `hyp` on `preterm`. Test the interaction with `testparm` and `lrtest`.

3. Check your answer using `effects`.

4. Use `regress` to find the effect of `gestwks` on `bweight` as a change in `bweight` per week of gestation.

5. Study whether this effect is modified by `sex` using `testparm`, and use the hash operator to find the sex specific effects of `gestwks`.

6. Check your answers using `effects`.

Chapter 16

Mantel-Haenszel methods

Mantel-Haenszel methods[9] were introduced in epidemiology as a way of controlling for potentially confounding variables in case-control studies by first creating strata based on these variables. Stratum-specific estimates of the effect of exposure, measured as odds ratios, are then obtained. Provided these are not too different, they are combined in a simple fashion, to provide a single estimate of exposure controlled for strata. The result is only an approximation to the fully efficient estimate provided by logistic regression, but because the method could be carried out by hand-calculator at a time when computers were not widely available, it became (and stayed) very popular. One particular benefit is that it can be used even when the individual strata contain very little data, as is the case with individually matched case-control studies.

16.1 The method

For an exposure with two levels the results for any given stratum can be summarized as an odds of D_1/H_1 for the exposed group in that stratum, and D_0/H_0 for the unexposed group in that stratum. Here D_1, H_1 refer to exposed cases (D for Deaths) and exposed controls (H for Healthy), respectively. Similarly D_0, H_0 refer to unexposed cases and controls. The odds ratio which measures the effect of exposure in the stratum is

$$\frac{D_1/H_1}{D_0/H_0} = \frac{D_1 H_0}{D_0 H_1}$$

In the Mantel–Haenszel method, these stratum-specific odds ratios are combined as

$$\frac{\sum D_1 H_0 / T}{\sum D_0 H_1 / T}$$

where summation is over strata, and $T = D_1 + H_1 + D_0 + H_0$, the total number of subjects in the stratum.

16.2 The Stata command

As an example we shall use the births data and look at the effect of `hyp` on `lowbw`, measured as an odds ratio and stratified by `sex`. Although this was not a case-control study, the effect of exposure was measured as an odds ratio, so the Mantel-Haenszel method can be applied. To see what the result should be, using `effects`, try

```
. use births, clear
. effects, res(lowbw) typ(binary) exp(hyp) exc str(sex) or
```

```
Level of sex        Effect
1                   5.316
2                   2.773
```

The effect of `hyp` as an odds ratio is 5.316 for the first stratum, and 2.773 for the second. To combine these and obtain the effect of `hyp` controlled for `sex`, try

```
. effects, res(lowbw) typ(binary) exp(hyp) exc catcon(sex) or
Levels      Effect
2/1         3.906
```

The same results can be obtained with

```
. logistic lowbw i.hyp i.sex
```

To do this with Mantel-Haenszel, try

```
. mhodds lowbw hyp, by(sex)
```

```
sex | Odds Ratio
----+-----------
  1 |   5.316129
  2 |   2.773333

Mantel-Haenszel estimate controlling for sex

  Odds Ratio
  ----------
    3.896980
```

In the `mhodds` command the first variable is the response (`lowbw`), the second is the exposure (`hyp`), and the stratifying variable (`sex`) is in the `by()`. The stratum specific odds ratios should be the same for the two methods, but the result of combining them using `mhodds` differs from the result using `effects` because the Mantel-Haenszel method is only an approximation to the regression methods on which `effects` is based. In fact the approximation is very good unless the stratum specific odds ratios are much larger or much less than 1.

To suppress the stratified effects (useful when there are lots of strata) put the stratifying variable after the exposure variable, as in

```
. mhodds lowbw hyp sex
```

To control for two variables it is necessary to create strata corresponding to all combinations of values of the two variables. For example, to control the effect of `hyp` on `lowbw` for both `sex` and `preterm`, avoiding missing values for `preterm`, try

```
. mhodds lowbw hyp, by(sex preterm)
```

Note that there are 4 strata corresponding to the 4 combinations of the 2 levels for `sex` and the 2 levels for `preterm`. To see the effects of `hyp` controlled for `sex` stratified by `preterm`, try

```
. mhodds lowbw hyp sex, by(preterm)
```

16.3 Exposures on more than two levels

Mantel-Haenszel methods can be used to deal with exposures on (say) three levels, by comparing level 2 with level 1 and then level 3 with level 1. The `mhodds` command must be run twice to do this. For example, try

```
. egen agegrp=cut(matage), at(20,30,40,50)
. mhodds lowbw agegrp, compare(30,20)
. mhodds lowbw agegrp, compare(40,20)
```

Note that the actual codes for the levels are used inside the `compare`. If the exposure is on more than two levels, and the `compare` is omitted, the exposure is assumed to be metric. For example,

```
. mhodds lowbw agegrp
```

shows that a one year increase in maternal age reduces the odds of low birth weight by a factor of $\times 0.9737$, very close the to value obtained with

```
. logit lowbw agegrp, or
```

16.4 Matched case-control studies

In matched case-control studies controls are deliberately matched to the cases on variables which are likely to confound the effect of exposure. When there are many small matched sets, as there are with individual matching, there are too many strata to use logistic regression to control for the matching, and, as we saw in Chapter 13, it is necessary to use conditional logistic regression instead. The Mantel-Haenszel method of controlling is in fact an approximation to the conditional likelihood used in `clogit` not the likelihood used in `logistic`. For this reason it can be used to analyse matched case-control studies in which there are many strata and not much data for each stratum. For example,

```
. use salmonella, clear
. mhodds case plant7 set
```

gives 4.58, very close to 4.47, the value obtained with `clogit`. It is best to suppress the stratum specific estimates by putting `set` after the exposure, not in `by( )`, because there are rather a lot of them.

Exercises

1. Load the births data set and use `mhodds` to find the effect of `hyp` on `preterm` as an odds ratio.

2. Cut `matage` into 2 groups with

   ```
   . egen mage2=cut(matage), at(20,40,45) label
   ```

   and use `mhodds` to study whether `mage2` modifies the effect of `hyp` on `preterm`.

3. Check your answer using `effects`.

Chapter 17

Survival data and stset

In this chapter you will learn how to declare data as st; how to summarize st data; how to use exponential regression to calculate rate ratios; how to split the follow-up time to take account of rates that vary during follow-up; how to use Cox regression to do the same on a continuous time scale; how to deal with exposures which change during follow-up, and how to deal with competing risks when calculating survival probabilities.

17.1 The response in survival data

The response in survival time data consists of two pieces of information – the time which the subject spends in the study, and what happens at the end of this time, usually held as a failure indicator. Stata has a family of commands, with names starting with st (where st stands for survival time), that deals with this type of data and for which the time and failure variables are specified once and for all using the command stset (survival time set). Once stset has been used the data are said to be in st form. Only then can the other st commands be used.

We shall illustrate this with a dataset called pbc.dta, which holds the data for 184 subjects who enrolled in a randomized clinical trial for the treatment of primary biliary cirrhosis, a chronic, but eventually fatal disease of the liver[1]. Load the PBC data and examine them with

```
. use pbc, clear
. describe
. tabulate d
```

Subjects were randomly allocated to two treatments, active and placebo, identified by the variable treat, coded 0 for placebo, 1 for active. The time variable (in years) is y and the failure variable is d, coded 1 for death from any cause, 0 otherwise. To declare the survival variables use

```
. stset y, fail(d)
```

where y is the time in the study and d is the failure indicator. The Stata output reports an overall summary. In this case there are 96 failures during a total follow–up time of 747 years so the overall rate is $96/747 = 0.129$ failures per year.

The failure variable is usually coded 1 for failure and 0 otherwise, but when different kinds of failure are recorded in the same study they would be coded with different numbers, e.g. the International Cause of Death code (ICD). To study the overall failure rate you would use `fail(d)` in the `stset` command, but to study any particular kind of failure, e.g. when d is coded 198, you would use `fail(d==198)`. This has the effect of making 198 the failure of interest and coding all other failures as censored.

17.2   Summarizing survival time

The distribution of survival time for the **pbc** data cannot be observed directly because of the subjects who have not failed by the end of the study. Instead we use the Kaplan-Meier survivor function, obtained with

```
. sts list
```

The first 5 columns of the first few lines of output look like this:

Time	Beg. Total	Fail	Net Lost	Survivor Function
.0219	184	0	1	1.0000
.0246	183	2	0	0.9891
.052	181	1	0	0.9836
.104	180	2	0	0.9727

where time is in years, so the earliest recorded time in the data is 0.0219 years, or 8 days. In the same row we read that 184 subjects were in the study just before time 0.0219 years, no one fails at that time, but one subject was lost (censored) at time 0.0219. Thereafter two fail (at time 0.0246), then one fails, then two fail, and so on.

The survivor function is the predicted probability that a new subject will survive a given time. To see how it is calculated, imagine that the time scale is divided into many tiny instants of time (e.g. hours), starting at time 0. The probabilities of failure and survival, referred to as P(F) and P(S) respectively, at each of the four instants recorded in the table are

Time	Beg. Total	Fail	Net Lost	P(F)	P(S)
.0219	184	0	1	0/184 = 0	1 – 0 = 1
.0246	183	2	0	2/183 = 0.0109	1 – 0.0109 = 0.9891
.052	181	1	0	1/181 = 0.0055	1 – 0.0055 = 0.9945
.104	180	2	0	2/180 = 0.0111	1 – 0.0111 = 0.9889

The survivor function for a given time is calculated by multiplying P(S) for all successive instants up to that time.

Time	Survivor function
.0219	1 = 1
.0246	1 x 0.9891 = 0.9891
.052	1 x 0.9891 x 0.9945 = 0.9836
.104	1 x 0.9891 x 0.9945 x 0.9889 = 0.9727

At first sight we seem to have forgotten the instants between the ones shown in the table, but because there are no deaths in these instants the survival probabilities corresponding to these instants are 1, and the survival function is not affected – it only changes its value at times when there are failures. For the same reason the survivor function does not change when there is a censoring event.

The actual values of the survivor function are useful when trying to understand the method, but in practice the graph of the survivor function is more useful. This is obtained with **sts**, the **st** survival command, which is an example of a command with several sub-commands such as **graph**. Try

```
. sts graph
```

to see the plot of the survivor function against time. The option

```
. sts graph, risktable
```

shows the number at risk at each of the time points ticked on the x-axis – the number of time points can be increased with

```
. sts graph, risktable xlabel(0(2)14)
```

The flat stretches of the plot correspond to periods of time during which there were no failures, and the drops occur at the times of the failures. From the graph, the predicted probability of surviving 2.6 years is 0.75, the predicted probability of surviving 5.4 years is 0.5, and the predicted probability of surviving 9.3 years years is 0.25. Another way of putting this is that a new subject will have a 25% chance of failing by 2.6 years, a 50% chance of failing by 5.4 years, and a 75% chance of failing by 9.3 years, and this is the summary produced by

```
. stsum
```

Note that it is not necessary to specify the survival variables with these commands because they have been specified with **stset**. Now try

```
. sts graph, by(treat)
```

to show the survival curves for the two treatment groups on the same graph, and

```
. stsum, by(treat)
```

to see the summary by treatment group. The median survival time is 5.3 years in the placebo group and 6.0 years, i.e. better, in the active treatment group.

17.3 Calculating rates and rate ratios

An alternative way of summarizing survival data is to calculate the rate at which failures are occurring, i.e. the number of failures per unit time. Try

```
. strate
```

which reports an overall rate of 0.129 deaths per year. To find the rate for each treatment group, try

```
. strate treat
```

The rate is higher for the placebo group. The units of the rate are taken from the units of the time variable declared in **stset**, i.e. **y** (coded in years), but they can be changed. To calculate rates per 10 years, try

```
. strate treat, per(10)
```

To calculate the rate ratio for active versus placebo treatment, together with a confidence interval, the command **streg** can be used. This command allows you to fit regression models to survival times. Because the distribution of survival time is generally skewed, **streg** fits regression models with distributions like exponential and lognormal. When the rate is constant over the entire follow-up time, the distribution of the survival time is exponential, so the appropriate form of the command on this assumption is

```
. streg i.treat, dist(exp)
```

Here the option **dist** stands for distribution and the argument **exp** stands for exponential. The estimated rate ratio for active versus placebo is 0.87, which is simply the ratio of the two yearly rates, 0.120 and 0.138. Note that the output refers to the Hazard Ratio, where hazard is an alternative word for rate. We would have obtained the same result using the **poisson** command introduced in Chapter 13. To see this, try

139

```
. poisson d i.treat, e(y) irr
```

Because `poisson` is not an `st` command it requires the failure variable `d` as response, and the follow-up time `y`.[1]

17.4   Cumulative rate plots

Imagine that time is divided into many very small bands, each of length h. For the PBC data, the first few bands in which there is a failure or loss are shown again below:

Time	Beg. Total	Fail	Net Lost
.0219	184	0	1
.0246	183	2	0
.052	181	1	0
.104	180	2	0

The estimated rate in any band is D/Y, where D is the number of failures in the band and Y the total follow-up during the band, so all bands which include no failures have a zero estimated rate. The band which includes the time 0.0246 has two failures, so the estimated rate is $2/(183h)$ (because $D = 2$ and $Y = 183h$) and so on. The *cumulative rate* or *hazard* is obtained by multiplying the rate in each band up to t, by the length of the band, and adding the results. Bands with no failures make no contribution, because their corresponding rate is zero, so the cumulative rate is zero up to time 0.0246, jumps to $2/183$ at time 0.0246, then jumps to $2/183 + 1/181$ at time 0.052, and so on. You can check this with

```
. sts list, cumhaz
```

The corresponding plot can be obtained with

```
. sts graph, cumhaz
```

When interpreting these plots it is useful to know that a straight line corresponds to a constant rate over time, and the rate is equal to the slope of the line. To use the plot to compare treatments, try

```
. sts graph, cumhaz by(treat)
```

You will see that the plot for the active group has a lower slope than the plot for the placebo group, i.e. the rate is lower in the active group than in the placebo group.

---

[1]Note that the default for `streg` is to report rate (i.e. hazard) ratios, while `poisson` reports log rate ratios and needs the option `irr` to report rate ratios.

17.5   Variables created by stset

When stset is used, up to five new variables are created for internal use: it is not necessary for the user to know about these variables, but it helps when trying to understand what is going on. The variables created in our example are:

_t0	time at entry
_t	time at exit
_d	failure indicator
_st	inclusion indicator

By default the time at entry is 0 so the time at exit is equal to the follow-up time. The failure indicator takes the value 1 for failures and 0 otherwise, and the inclusion indicator, _st, flags all subjects to be included in any following st commands. Try

```
. use pbc, clear
. stset y, fail(d)
. browse id _t0 y _t d _d _st
```

to see the values these variables take for the PBC data. You will see that _t0 is always zero, _t is the same as y, and _d is the same as d. The variable _st is 1 for all observations, which means they are all included. When an observation is excluded from the analysis for some reason, the value of _st is set to 0.

17.6   Rates that vary with time

In many applications the rates are not constant over the entire time in the study. One way of dealing with this is to split time into bands short enough to assume that during each band of follow-up the rate is constant (although it may change from one band to the next), and to estimate rates separately for each band. To split the times of the PBC data we need the command stsplit, but first we need to stset the data again so that the option id is included:

```
. stset y, fail(d) id(id)
```

The option id( ) declares the name of the variable which holds the subjects' identifiers, also called id in this dataset, so that when the individual times are split they can still be linked back to the original subject. In order to see what happens we list the information for subject 45 before the split:

```
. list id _t0 _t _d if id==45, noobs
  id   _t0           _t   _d
  -------------------------
  45     0   5.3114305    1
```

Then we split the follow-up into (say) 2-year bands with a 4-year band at the end (from 8 to 12 years), and list again with:

```
. stsplit timeband, at(0,2,4,6,8,12) trim
. list id _t0 _t _d timeband if id==45,noobs
  id    _t0           _t    _d    timeband
  -------------------------------------------
  45     0             2     0         0
  45     2             4     0         2
  45     4      5.3114305    1         4
```

Subject 45 spent 5.3 years in the study and this time has been split into 2 years in the band 0–2, at the end of which the subject was still alive ($\_d=0$), 2 years in the band 2–4, at the end of which the subject was still alive ($\_d=0$), and a last period of 1.3 years (from 4 to 5.3) in the band 4–6 at the end of which the subject failed ($\_d=1$). The points at which time is split are defined by $at(\ldots)$, and the option trim makes sure that no follow-up time outside the range specified is included. The word timeband following stsplit declares the name to be given to the new variable that identifies the bands. This takes the value of the lower end of each band. Try

```
. tabulate timeband
```

which shows the values taken by timeband. It also shows that, although to begin with there were 184 subjects, after splitting their times there are 466 observations, i.e. around 2.5 per subject. The overall information on the follow-up times and failures of these subjects has not been corrupted however: it has only changed format. Try

```
. tabulate _d
```

and you will see that there are still only 96 failures.

The reason for using stsplit was to find the timeband-specific yearly rates, which you can do with

```
. strate timeband
```

These rates can be also plotted by adding the option graph:

```
. strate timeband, graph
```

To look at the effect of treatment stratified by timeband, try

```
. streg i.timeband i.treat#i.timeband, dist(exp)
```

The part of the output which reports the effects of treat (level 1 vs level 0) in the different timebands is shown below:

```
treat#timeband |
           1 0 |    1.152357
           1 2 |    1.028036
           1 4 |     .5414798
           1 6 |     .5234707
           1 8 |     .5475632
```

The treatment appears to have no effect up to 4 years, with a beneficial effect after this. To test the equality of these 5 effects with a Wald test, try

. `testparm treat#timeband, equal`

where the option `equal` tests that these five effects are equal to each other, rather than jointly equal to zero. This test provides no evidence for such time-changing effects (p=0.57), so we should assume a constant effect of treatment, and control for `timeband` using

. `streg i.treat i.timeband, dist(exp)`

The effect of treatment is 0.839, not very different from the original overall rate ratio of 0.87.

17.7   Cox regression

Sometimes rates vary so quickly with time that it would be necessary to split the follow-up into many pieces. In these situations, if we are only interested in estimating the rate ratio between different groups controlled for time, we can use `stcox` to fit what is generally called Cox regression, or the proportional hazards model. This is very similar to the Poisson regression model

$$\ln(\lambda) = \alpha + \beta X$$

introduced in Chapter 13. More precisely the Poisson model is

$$\ln(\lambda_X) = \alpha + \beta X$$

in which λ_X is the rate for subjects taking the value X for the explanatory variable, and α is the value of $\ln(\lambda_X)$ when $X = 0$, i.e. $\ln(\lambda_0)$. With this notation

$$\ln(\lambda_X) = \ln(\lambda_0) + \beta X$$

which can also be written

$$\ln(\lambda_X/\lambda_0) = \beta X$$

showing that the parameter β is the effect of a unit increase in X on the log rate (or hazard) ratio. The parameter λ_0 is called the baseline rate. Further explanatory variables can be added to the right hand side of the equation.

In the Cox model the two rates λ_X and λ_0 vary with time, and the model is written as

$$\ln(\lambda_X^t/\lambda_0^t) = \beta X$$

The assumption of proportional hazards states that the rate ratio λ_X^t/λ_0^t does not depend on t which is why the parameter β is written without a t.

To use the Cox model to find the effect of treatment controlled for time (continuously), try

```
. use pbc, clear
. stset y, fail(d)
. stcox i.treat
```

and you will see that the rate ratio (hazard ratio) is 0.856, but no baseline parameters are reported. This is because the baseline parameters are not estimated in Cox regression, only the β parameter. It is important to remember that the rate ratio 0.856 is controlled for time in study, even though no baseline parameters are estimated. To plot the survival curve predicted by a fitted Cox model try

```
. stcox i.treat
. stcurve, survival at1(treat=0) at2(treat=1)
```

The value 0.856 from Cox regression is close to 0.839, the value obtained using streg with i.treat and i.timeband. Using smaller and smaller time-bands in stsplit, the result from streg gets closer and closer to the result from stcox. The main difference between these two approaches is that with Cox regression we can ignore how rates change with time, and they can vary freely, while with streg rates are assumed to be constant or to vary in pre-specified steps. However, both regression methods assume that the rate ratio between the two groups is constant over the follow-up time, and both report the effect of treat controlled for time; stcox controls for time continuously, while splitting the data and using streg with timeband as one of the explanatory variables in the model controls for time in bands.

17.8 Checking the proportional hazards assumption

Checking on the proportional hazards assumption is straightforward when the rate ratio is estimated for each timeband, and it is only a question of looking at these to see whether they are approximately the same. When using stcox to estimate the hazard ratio for two groups, it is possible to check on proportional hazards by plotting the cumulative hazard against time, on a log scale, for each group, with

```
. sts, cumhaz by(treat) ylog
```

The two curves should be parallel if the proportional hazards assumption is true. In this case the hazards seem very close up to about 4 years and then diverge after that. In other words the effect of treatment seems to be modified by time in study.

Another way to check the proportionality assumption with a graph is with the so-called 'log-log' plot. Try

```
. stphplot, by(treat)
```

This shows the negative of the cumulative hazard function on a log scale (i.e. -ln-ln(survival)) versus time, also on a log scale. Again, if the curves were parallel, there would be graphical evidence of proportionality. Alternatively, to test whether there is effect modification on a continuous time scale, you can use the Schoenfeld test. This is based on the scaled Schoenfeld residuals which can be generated when a Cox model is fitted. If there are several explanatory variables in the model, there is a set of residuals for each variable. If the residuals show a significant linear trend with time, there is evidence of lack of proportionality. Try

```
. stcox i.treat
. estat phtest
```

To plot the residuals against time try

```
. estat phtest, plot(1.treat)
```

which shows no evidence of departure from the proportionality assumption.

17.9   A metric exposure

The PBC data contains a variable measuring the bilirubin at entry for each patient. To see the effect of this measurement on the mortality rate we shall regard it as the exposure, so the exposure is now metric. We start by looking at the distribution of bilirubin with

```
. cdfplot bilirub
```

You will see that 90% of subjects have a bilirubin below 200 mumol/l, while 10% have values between 200 and 600. A few high values like these can have a strong influence on the estimated effect of a change in bilirubin, so it is better to use the logarithm of bilirubin when fitting models in which bilirubin is metric (i.e. not grouped). This is easily done with

```
. generate logbili=ln(bilirub)
```

and using `logbili` in place of `bilirub`. To find the effect of `logbili`, controlled for time continuously, try

```
. stcox logbili
```

which shows that the effect of a unit increase in `logbili` (measured at entry) is to increase the rate by a factor of 2.64.

17.10   Time updated exposures

The exposure `treat` does not change with time, but `bilirub` does, and the file `pbcfu.dta` contains the updated values, taken at around 6 monthly intervals during the trial (at least during the first years). Each observation corresponds to a band of time starting at the time the bilirubin measurement is taken. Try

```
. use pbcfu, clear
. list if id==45, noobs clean
    id     treat   band   d        time    bilirub
    45   placebo      1   0    .4982888         19
    45   placebo      2   0    3.613963         83
    45   placebo      3   1     5.31143         83
```

and you will that there are three observations, one for each time band. The first band for subject 45 runs from 0 to 0.498 and the bilirubin value measured at the start of this band was 19. The second band runs from 0.498 to 3.613 and the bilirubin measured at the start of this band was 83, and so on. The subject survives the first two bands but fails at the end of the third. To `stset` these data, and to see the resulting `st` variables try

```
. stset time, fail(d) id(id)
. list id time d _* if id==45
```

You will see that `_t0` contains the time when each time band starts (assuming the first starts at 0) while `_t` contains the time at the end. Because the `id` was specified in the `stset` command all `st` commands know that these 3 observations come from the same subject. To find the effects of `logbili` using the time updated values, and controlling for time continuously, try

```
. gen logbili=ln(bilirub)
. stcox logbili
```

The effect of updated log bilirubin is 2.32.

17.11   Competing risks

In some studies there are two or more kinds of failure, and each blocks the others from happening, so the different kinds of failure are in competition with each other. This situation is usually referred to as *competing risks* (or competing events). The rate at which each different kind of failure occurs can still be estimated by coding the survival time for all other types of failure as censored, it should be borne in mind that each of these estimated rates is conditional on the subject having survived all the other kinds of failure.

The same methods can be used to study a failure rate in the presence of competing risks as in a study without competing risks, but problems arise when the results are expressed as survival probabilities. Now the Kaplan-Meier (KM) survival curve for failure of a particular type, A, is inappropriate because this curve refers to survival in a population in which A is the only kind of failure. To see how to calculate the correct survival probabilities we shall first express the KM survival probabilities in terms of failure probabilities.

Let $t_1, t_2, t_3, \cdots$ be the times of failure from A, and let p_i be the probability of failure from A in a small band of time around t_i, given the subject has survived A up until the previous band. Then the probabilities of failure from A at times $t_1, t_2, t_3, \cdots$ are

$$p_1, \quad (1-p_1)p_2, \quad (1-p_1)(1-p_2)p_3, \quad \cdots$$

respectively, and zero in bands between these times. The probability of failure at any time up to and including t_k is the sum of these probabilities up to t_k. This is called the cumulative incidence for failure from A at t_k, and the probability of surviving beyond t_k is 1 minus this cumulative incidence. That this gives the KM survival probabilities is clear from the fact that the cumulative incidence up and including t_3 (for example) is

$$p_1 + (1-p_1)p_2 + (1-p_1)(1-p_2)p_3$$

and 1 minus this is easily shown to be

$$(1-p_1)(1-p_2)(1-p_3)$$

which is the probability of surviving beyond t_3.

Now suppose there are competing risks, and let q_i be the probability of failure from any of the risks competing with A in a band around t_i, given the subject has survived up until the band before. Then the probabilities of failure from A at times $t_1, t_2, t_3, \cdots$ are

$$p_1, \quad (1-p_1-q_1)p_2, \quad (1-p_1-q_1)(1-p_2-q_2)p_3, \quad \cdots$$

respectively, because the subject must survive the competing risks as well as A. The cumulative incidence of failure from A is found from the sum of these probabilities up to t_k, and the probability of surviving beyond t_k is calculated as 1 minus the cumulative incidence up to t_k. When there are no competing risks all the q's are zero and you get the same answer as from Kaplan-Meier. Otherwise the true cumulative incidence is always less than the cumulative incidence which ignores the competing risks.

The command `stcompet` can be used to calculate the cumulative incidence, and should be used in place of `sts graph` when there are competing risks. It is included with the files which came with this book, but can also be installed with

`. ssc install stcompet, replace`

To illustrate this command we shall use the `hiv_si` data set discussed by Putter et. al.[12] in their tutorial on competing risks in Statistics in Medicine, and also referred to in the Stata pdf documentation. These data refer to two possible events following HIV infection: the first is the appearance of the SI phenotype (an indicator of poor prognosis), the second is AIDS. When analysing time to occurrence of SI before AIDS is diagnosed, AIDS acts as a competing event. To inspect these data, try

```
. use hiv_si, clear
. describe
```

The variable `status` is coded 0 for censored, 1 for AIDS and 2 for SI. To `stset` the data with SI as the event of interest, try

```
. stset time, fail(status==2)
```

To declare AIDS as a competing event, and then to calculate the cumulative incidence and the survival probabilities for SI, try

```
. stcompet ci=ci, compet1(1)
. gen sp=1-ci
```

where `ci` is the name of a new variable which contains the cumulative incidence, also called `ci`, calculated by `stcompet`. To plot the survival probabilities against time try

```
. line sp time if status==2, c(J) sort
```

Note that the cumulative incidence for each type of failure is included in the results of `stcompet` so the restriction `if status==2` is necessary to plot the survival probability for SI. This plot should be compared with

```
. sts graph
```

the Kaplan-Meier estimates of the probabilities of survival from SI. It goes to 0 at around 14 years because the very last patient at risk at 14 years suffers the SI event (check this with `.   sts list`).

In general one should not draw survival curves when data are sparse. For this reason we restrict the time scale to a range where, say, at least 10 individuals are at risk. In this example this would correspond to times from 0 to 13.4 years. To make the comparison clearer the two survival curves can be put on the same graph with

```
. sts gen kmsp=s
. twoway (line sp time if status==2, c(J) sort)(line kmsp time, c(J) sort)
         if time<13.5, xline(10) ylabel(0(.2)1,angle(h))
```

Here the option `ylabel(0(.2)1,angle(h))` has been added to improve the look of the plot. The $S(t+0)$ on the graph refers to the KM probability of surviving beyond t. The probability of surviving 10 years is roughly 0.7 from the KM curve (`kmsp`, where

SI is the only kind of failure) and 0.6 from the `sp` curve (where subjects can also fail from AIDS), showing that the KM survival curve overestimates the true survival probability.

Survival curves can be calculated separately for different groups. For example, to compare the survival from SI by whether `ccr5` is coded 0 or 1, i.e. whether a particular gene does not (WW) or does (WM) have a deletion, try

```
. twoway (line sp time if ccr5==0 & status==2, c(J) sort)
         (line sp time if ccr5==1 & status==2, c(J) sort) if time<13.5,
         legend(label(1 "WW") label(2 "WM")) ylabel(0(.2)1,angle(h))
```

The corresponding cumulative incidence curves can be compared in the same way by replacing `sp` with `ci`.

17.12   Further reading

For further reading about survival analysis we recommend *An Introduction to Survival Analysis for Stata, Revised Edition.*[3] For a discussion of regression models for competing risks refer to the material on `stcrreg` in the Stata documentation.

Exercises

1. Load the `cancer.dta` dataset. How many deaths occurred during the study?

2. Now `stset` the data and find the median survival time for each drug type. Plot the survival curves for the three groups.

3. Obtain the Nelson-Aalen plots for the three groups. What are your preliminary conclusions?

4. Find the rates of death for each drug type, per year, assuming a constant rate over follow-up.

5. Find the rate ratios for each of the active drugs compared with placebo using `streg`.

6. Break the follow-up time into 5 intervals, from 0 to 24 months in 6 month time-bands and then from 24 to 40 months. Call this variable `timeband`. Find the overall rates of death for each time-band, per year.

7. Use `streg` to find the effect of each active drug compared with placebo, controlled for `timeband`.

8. Use `stcox` to find the effect of each active drug compared with placebo.

Chapter 18

Different time scales and standardization

In clinical follow-up studies time is usually recorded as time since entry to the study, but in population studies time is more likely to be recorded as calendar time, i.e. as date of entry to the study and date of exit. Another difference is that in clinical follow-up studies the time since entry is usually the most important determinant of the rate of interest, whereas in population studies other time scales, such as age, may be more important. To deal with this `stset` has options to change the time scale used for analysis. In this chapter we explore these options.

18.1 Follow-up time

No matter how time is originally recorded it is always possible to calculate follow-up time and to use it as the time variable. For example, in the diet data, the variable y was calculated from `(dox - doe)/365.25` and added to the data set. This measures follow-up time in years, using 365.25 as the average number of days in a year. Using this variable, and the failure variable `chd`, we can calculate rates and rate ratios with

```
. use diet, clear
. stset y, fail(chd)
. strate hieng, per(1000)
. streg i.hieng, dist(exp)
```

By starting in this way we are using the time since entry in years as the time scale, but it is better to `stset` using the original time variables `dox` and `doe` because then we can consider other time scales as well. To do this, try

```
. stset dox, fail(chd) origin(time mdy(1,1,1900)) enter(doe)
      id(id) scale(365.25)
```

where we have included id(id) in case we need to split the data later. What stset does is to create new exit and entry times (you don't have to type these)

```
_t  = (dox - origin)/scale
_t0 = (doe - origin)/scale
```

from dox and doe using the new origin and scale. Two points about the stset command are worth noting. The first is the origin of the original time scale is at 1/1/1960, but this has been shifted to mdy(1,1,1900), an operation which needed the keyword time. The reason for this is that some subjects entered the study before 1/1/1960, and stset ignores follow-up time before the origin. The second is that the option scale(365.25) converts days to years. To see the effect of this stset on the underlying variables, try

```
. list id _t0 _t if id==163
    id          _t0          _t
  ---------------------------
   163   60.788501   74.157426
```

Remembering that time is now measured in years from 1/1/1900, you see that subject 163 enters the study towards the end of 1960, and develops CHD at the beginning of 1974. The follow-up time is therefore $74.157 - 60.788 = 13.369$ years. To calculate rates per 1000 years, try

```
. strate, per(1000)
```

which shows that the overall rate is 9.99 per 1000 years. Similarly

```
. strate hieng, per(1000)
```

shows the rates for the two levels of hieng, and

```
. streg i.hieng, dist(exp)
```

shows the rate ratio.

18.2   Rates that change with time

In the above analysis the rates are overall rates, and we have made no effort to see whether they change with time, or to control rate ratios for time. Before doing this we should consider which time scale to use. The calendar time scale was that used to record the data, but calendar time may not be a major determinant of the rate. Age is likely to be more important. We can change the time scale from calendar time to age by re-defining the origin as the date of birth (held in dob):

```
. streset, origin(dob)
. list id _t0 _t _d if id==163, noobs
. strate, per(1000)
. strate hieng, per(1000)
```

Redefining the origin changes _t0 and _t but does not change the overall rates because these depend only on the times between entry and exit, not on the origin.

To study how rates change with age we shall split the follow–up on the age scale using 5-year age bands. First check that the data are **stset** properly with

```
. stset
```

which should show that the origin is **dob** and that the time of entry is **doe**. If this is not the case, you will need to start again with

```
. stset dox, fail(chd) origin(dob) enter(doe) id(id) scale(365.25)
```

We now split the follow-up, ignoring the follow-up time before age 45 with the option **trim** (there was only one failure before this age and we shall ignore this for the sake of simplicity). [1] Before and after doing this we check on subject 163 to see the effects of the split:

```
. list id _t0 _t _d if id==163, noobs
. stsplit ageband, at(45(5)70) trim
. list id _t0 _t _d ageband if id==163, noobs
```

Before the split, the listing was

```
 id          _t0              _t    _d
------------------------------------
163    47.55373     60.922656      1
```

This shows that subject 163 entered at age 47.55 and left at age 60.92 when he developed CHD. After the split, the listing is

```
 id          _t0              _t    _d
------------------------------------
163    47.55373              50     0
163          50              55     0
163          55              60     0
163          60     60.922656       1
```

which shows that the single observation for subject 163 has been replaced by four: the first covering the age band 45–49, the second covering 50–54, the third covering 55–59, and the fourth covering 60–64. The subject spends only 0.92 years in the final age band before developing CHD. Altogether 858 new observations have been created by this **stsplit**. To produce age–specific rates, try

---

[1] Any observations referring to age before 45 will have _st set to 0, and will be excluded from any further **st** analyses.

```
. strate ageband, per(1000)
```

You can obtain a graph of the rates with

```
. strate ageband, per(1000) graph
```

Now try

```
. strate, per(1000)
```

and you will see that the overall rates have changed slightly from 9.99/1000, because some of the follow-up time has been trimmed by the `stplit` command and one event has been lost.

To look at the effect of `hieng` stratified by `ageband`, try

```
. streg i.ageband i.hieng#i.ageband, dist(exp)
```

and to check that the effects are the same in all age bands, try

```
. testparm i.hieng#i.ageband, equal
```

There is no evidence that the effects of `hieng` are modified by `ageband`, so we can find the effect of `hieng` controlled for `ageband` with

```
. streg i.hieng i.ageband, dist(exp)
```

which gives 0.539.

18.3   Two time-scales

To see how rates are changing jointly with two time scales we need to split the follow-up time on both scales. To split the diet data on both age and calendar period at pre-defined times, first split on age with

```
. use diet, clear
. stset dox, fail(chd) origin(dob) entry(doe) scale(365.25) id(id)
. stsplit ageband, at(40(5)70) trim
```

To re-set the origin, having already split the follow-up time, the option `after()` is required.[2] To split the data on calendar period, again using 5-year bands, try

```
. stsplit period, after(time=mdy(1,1,1900)) at(50(5)80) trim
. replace period = period + 1900
```

After this last split the variable `period` takes the value 50 for the calendar period 1950-54, 55 for 1955-59, etc., so for clarity, we have added 1900 to these values. After inspecting the results with

---

[2]You cannot reset the origin and then split because this will also reset _st to 1, so follow-up which was trimmed in the first split will be included in the second.

```
. list id _t0 _t _d ageband period if id==163, noobs
```

you will see there are now 6 observations for subject 163. To calculate rates by age, try

```
. strate ageband, per(1000)
```

To calculate rates by calendar period, try

```
. strate period, per(1000)
```

To find the effect of **hieng** controlled for both **ageband** and **period**, try

```
. streg i.hieng i.ageband i.period, dist(exp)
```

The answer is 0.552.

The command **strate** can only produce one-way tables of rates, so to produce two-way tables we need to use **tabmore**, which is a non-st command. First generate new failure and time variables, taking care only to include observations with **_st==1**:

```
. generate D = _d if _st==1
. generate Y = _t - _t0 if _st==1
```

Then produce tables of rates per 1000, by age and period, with

```
. tabmore, res(D) typ(failure) row(ageband) col(period) rate fup(Y)
```

18.4   Standardization

Mortality and incidence rates for many diseases vary strongly with age, and it is always necessary, when comparing rates between different groups of subjects, to control such comparisons for age. In the early days of epidemiology this was done with direct and indirect standardization, techniques still widely used today.

Direct standardization

In direct standardization the age–specific rates found in each of the groups being compared are applied to a population with a standard age distribution in order to predict the number of deaths (mortality studies) or new cases (incidence studies) that would have occurred in that population. Two commonly used standard age distributions are those of Europe and the World. The total number of deaths expected in a standard population of size (say) 100 000, using the age–specific rates for a study group, is the directly standardized rate per 100 000 for that study group. We shall illustrate the process with an example.

Data for mortality in England and Wales County Boroughs and Rural Districts for 1936 are in the file **cbrd.dta**, where the variable **place** is coded **cb** for country boroughs and `rd` for rural districts. The problem is to compare the mortality between these two places taking account of differences in age. First load these data and see how they are organized. Then find the total deaths and total population, by place, and hence the two crude death rates per 1000, with

```
. use cbrd, clear
. collapse (sum) deaths pop, by(place)
. gen crude_rate=deaths/pop*1000
. list
```

To take account of possible differences in age structure between County Boroughs and Rural Districts we shall standardize the rates for age using the world population, which is in the file `stndpop`. Load the `cbrd` data, create a `rate` variable (per 1000), and merge with the standard population in `stndpop`, using `agegrp` as the key variable:

```
. describe using stndpop
. use cbrd, clear
. generate rate = deaths/pop*1000
. merge m:1 agegrp using stndpop
```

To directly standardize the rates, and compare them with the crude ones, try

```
. gen dst_rate=rate*wt
. collapse (sum) deaths pop dst_rate, by(place)
. gen crude_rate =deaths/pop*1000
. list place crude_rate dst_rate ,noobs
```

Indirect standardization

Indirect standardization is used when the study groups being compared are small, so that their age–specific rates are unreliable. In this case standard age–specific reference rates are used in place of a standard age distribution. For each of the study groups being compared the standard rates are used to predict the number of cases expected in each age–group. The total expected cases for a group is compared with the total observed cases to give a standardized ratio (observed/expected). In the case of mortality this is called the standardized mortality ratio (SMR).

We return to the 1936 mortality data for County Boroughs and Rural Districts in England and Wales. To carry out indirect standardization we use the England and Wales standard rates for the period 1901–1910, which are in `stndrate.dta`. Load the data from `cbrd`, merge with the standard rates using `agegrp` as key variable, and calculate the expected number of deaths from standard rates for each `agegrp` and `place` and with

```
. describe using stndrate
. use cbrd, clear
```

```
. merge m:1 agegrp using stndrate
. gen exp=rate*pop/1000
```

Then sum both observed and expected deaths over `agegrp`, and hence calculate the SMR for county boroughs and rural districts with

```
. collapse (sum) deaths exp, by(place)
. gen smr=deaths/exp
. list
```

You can do all this with the command `smrby`[3], as follows:

```
. use cbrd, clear
. merge m:1 agegrp using stndrate
. gen exp=rate*pop/1000
. smrby deaths exp, by(place)
```

Exercises

1. The file `mortality.dta` contains the deaths and population for Sweden and Panama, by age. Find the crude death rate per 100 000 for each country. The file `stndpop3.dta` contains the standard world population for the same age groups. Find the directly standardized rates for Sweden and Panama using this standard population.

2. The file `asthma.dta` contains data for the 403 counties of England and Wales which are to be compared in respect of deaths from asthma, recorded over a period of 5 years. Load the data and describe them. For each county and age–sex group the variable `pop` contains the number of subjects alive at the middle of the 5 year period and the variable `deaths` contains the number of deaths during the 5 year period. The file is sorted on `age` and `sex`. The total time spent in the study is approximately the mid–year population × 5 years, which is in the variable `pyrs`.

   (a) Find the crude rates per 100 000 for each county.

   (b) To obtain standardized mortality ratios for asthma, first have a look at the file `ewrate_asthma.dta`. The variable `rate` contains the reference rate (per 100 000), for each age–sex group, for the period of the study. Then merge `asthma.dta` with `ewrate_asthma.dta`, and calculate the expected deaths for each county. Use `collapse` to sum the observed and expected deaths over counties and calculate the SMR's. You will see a wide variation in SMR, from 0 to around 2.5.

---

[3]The command `smrby` is not part of official Stata, and is not on the SSC site, but it is included with the files that come with the book.

Chapter 19

Meta-analysis

This chapter covers the `metan` command for calculating summary estimates from a set of similar studies and displaying them graphically, the `metareg` command for exploring any heterogeneity present among the study specific estimates, and the `metabias` and `metafunnel` commands for exploring whether selection of studies included in the meta-analysis depends on their being more extreme. These commands were all written by users and are described in detail in Sterne (2009)[14].

19.1 Background

The aim of a meta-analysis is to summarise the evidence gathered in several studies on an effect of interest. Such effects could be measures of treatment efficacy from randomized clinical trials or associations derived from observational studies. Although very popular, the result from meta-analysis can be controversial if some of the contributing studies are deemed to be of poor quality or if the summarised effect is thought not to be representative of the separate effects. For this reason meta-analyses should always be preceded by systematic reviews of the evidence, with searches guided by pre-defined protocols and should include unpublished data to avoid publication bias. Summary estimates should be calculated only if the study specific effects appear to be fairly similar.

Start by installing the relevant packages with

```
. ssc install metan, replace
. ssc install metareg, replace
. ssc install metabias, replace
. ssc install metafunnel, replace
```

These files are also included with the files which came with the book, but installing them from the SSC website ensures you have the latest versions.[1]

19.2 Data

Usually the data consist of one observation per contributing study. This should hold details of the study i.e. the study identifier and year of publication, plus its reported effect with a measure of its precision (standard error or confidence interval). The effect of interest depends of the type of response: if the response is metric the effect is the difference in means; if binary it is an odds ratio, etc. For reasons seen in chapter 14 log transformations of odds ratios, risk ratios and rate ratios are preferred when carrying out inferences, and this applies to meta-analyses too.

The BCG trial data set holds the results of 11 published placebo randomized trials of BCG, a tuberculosis (TB) vaccine (Colditz et al., 1994[4]). Load the data and list the main variables with

```
. use bcgtrial, clear
. describe
. list trial trialnam tcases tnoncases ccases cnoncases, noobs clean
```

The observations are sorted according to the year the trial started and, if more than one trial started in the same year, by first author. The response is binary, being a TB case, and the measure of effect is the odds ratio. We calculate the log odds ratio and its standard error for each trial with

```
. gen lnOR= ln( (tcases/tnoncases)/(ccases/cnoncases) )
. gen se_lnOR= sqrt((1/tcases)+(1/tnoncases)+(1/ccases)+(1/cnoncases))
```

where `tcases tnoncases ccases cnoncases` are the numbers of exposed (i.e. *treated*) cases and non-cases and the number of unexposed (i.e. *control*) cases and non-cases. We can then view the study results graphically with what is known as a *forest plot*:

```
. metan lnOR se_lnOR, eform nooverall nobox
```

The option `eform` tells Stata to report effects in their original scale (`eform` stands for 'exponentiated form'). Because Stata does not know whether what is exponentiated is an odds ratio, risk ratio or rate ratio, the heading of the plot is generic, "ES", standing for Exponentiated Statistic. The options `nooverall` and `nobox` remove the summary estimate which we do not want yet. The horizontal lines attached to each study specific effect represent the 95% confidence intervals that are calculated using the standard errors. You can improve the labels used in the plot with

```
. metan lnOR se_lnOR, eform nooverall nobox xlabel(0.1,5)
```

---

[1]To find out what is on the SSC site, eg for commands starting with "m" type `ssc describe m`, or search more generally, using the Stata help facilities, with `findit meta`.

and add trial names (held in a string variable) with

```
. metan lnOR se_lnOR, eform nooverall nobox xlabel(0.1,5)
      label(namevar=trialnam)
```

When the response is binary, as in this case, you can avoid the need to calculate the effect measure and its SE by using the command in the form:

```
. metan tcases tnoncases ccases cnoncases, or nooverall nobox
      xlabel(0.1,5) label(namevar=trialnam)
```

where the option `or` is necessary to specify the effect measure which is to be used in creating the plot. Note that the effect column is now labelled OR.

19.3   Pooled effect

There are two main ways to summarize (or pool) the separate study effects. The first uses a weighted average of the separate effects and is known as the *fixed effects* approach. This is based on the assumption that each study measures the same effect, with the weighted average estimating this common effect. Different types of weights can be used. The alternative way allows the true effects in each study to differ according to some well-behaved distribution, and the mean of this distribution is then used to summarize the separate study effects. This is the *random effects* approach.

With either approach it does not makes sense to look at summaries of very different effects, so the first thing to do is to check that the observed study effects are not too dissimilar, i.e. are not *heterogeneous*. For this reason before producing any overall summary measure of effect we explore the degree of heterogeneity across the studies. The forest plot of the BCG trials shows a large degree of heterogeneity and this can be assessed formally using either the Q or the I^2 statistic. The Q statistic is based on the squared differences between each study effect and their fixed effect average, and I^2 is derived from Q and is interpreted as the proportion of total variability explained by heterogeneity. If the studies are homogenous both should be small. Both statistics are calculated by `metan` when we drop the `nooverall` option. To avoid producing yet another plot we also replace the graph options `nobox` and `xlabel(0.1,5)` with `nograph`:

```
. metan lnOR se_lnOR, eform nograph  label(namevar=trialnam)
```

Both Q and I^2 are very large, in line with the high degree of heterogeneity shown in the plot.

19.4   Fixed effect summary

Fixed effect summaries are produced using a weighted average of the separate study effects. When using the general format of `metan` the weights are equal to the inverse variance of the separate study effects, i.e. to $1/\text{SE}^2$ where SE refers to the SE of the separate study effects. When the effects are rate ratios or odds ratios, as in this example, the SE refers to the effect expressed on a log scale. Earlier we used

```
. metan lnOR se_lnOR, eform nooverall nobox xlabel(0.1,5)
    label(namevar=trialnam)
```

to produce a forest plot without the overall summary, whereas in

```
. metan lnOR se_lnOR, eform xlabel(0.1,5) label(namevar=trialnam) fixed
```

the forest plot shows a fixed effect summary based on inverse variance (I-V) weights. The centre of the diamond box at the bottom of the plot corresponds to the summary value of 0.729 while the width of the diamond shows the 95% confidence interval $(0.665, 0.799)$. This plot also uses boxes to report the separate study effects, with sizes proportional to the corresponding weights. The last study, called Madras, is the one with the largest weight and therefore with the largest influence on the overall average. Note that all this information is also reported in the output table.

When metan is used with the tcases tnoncases ccases cnoncases format there is a choice of weights to produce the fixed effect summary when the raw data are available. The default weights now are those used in the Mantel-Haenszel method for pooling stratum-specific effects, where the strata are the separate studies (see Chap 16). There is some advantage in being able to use M-H weights because these can be calculated for very small studies where the I-V weights cannot because one or more of tcases tnoncases ccases cnoncases is zero. Try

```
. metan tcases tnoncases ccases cnoncases, or xlabel(0.1,5)
    label(namevar=trialnam) fixed
```

The summary estimate is different from the one produced when using the general format of metan because here the weights are based on the Mantel-Haenszel (M-H) method (0.695 instead of 0.729). To use the I-V weights and find the same result as before try,

```
. metan tcases tnoncases ccases cnoncases, or xlabel(0.1,5)
    label(namevar=trialnam) fixedi
```

where the i in fixedi stands for *inverse-variance*. Another option when the metan command is used with the tcases tnoncases ccases cnoncases format is peto for Peto's weights.

19.5   Random effects summary

Assume that each true effect, e.g. each study log OR, comes from a normal distribution with variance τ^2. This variance is called the *between study variance*. The random effects weight for each study then takes the form

$$\frac{1}{\text{SE}^2 + \tau^2}$$

where SE is the standard error of the estimated effect for that study. To calculate these weights, τ^2 is estimated from the Q statistic. This approach is called the DerSimonian and Laird (D+L) method, and is incorporated into the `metan` command with the option `random`. Try,

```
. metan tcases tnoncases ccases cnoncases, or
        label(namevar=trialnam) random
```

which bases the calculation of the Q statistic on the M-H weights. To force the use of I-V weights, use the option `randomi` in place of `random`. In this example the results are very similar, and the large variation in study specific effects is reflected by the large between study variance of 0.39, reported at the bottom of the results. As a consequence, the study specific boxes shown in the plot are less variable than before and studies which had the larger fixed-effect weights, e.g. Madras, have much reduced influence on the random effect summary because of the inclusion of the between study variance in the weight calculation. In general, smaller studies, which have little influence in fixed effect summaries become more influential in their random effects counterparts, especially when τ^2 is large.

You can see the two diamonds side by side, one for random effects pooling and one for fixed effects pooling, with

```
. metan lnOR se_lnOR, eform  label(namevar=trialnam)
        random second(fixed)
```

where the fixed effect summary, and the Q-statistics for the random effect summary, are both based on I-V weights. As expected, the random effects diamond is much wider than the fixed effects one, due to the between studies variability.

19.6   Sources of heterogeneity

The data set `bw_bc` holds the effect of (metric) birth weight on breast cancer incidence calculated in 24 studies (13 cohort and 11 matched and unmatched case-control studies [6]). Start by loading and describing the data with

```
. use bw_bc, clear
. describe
```

Tabulating the variable `study_type` with

```
. tabulate study_type
```

we see that there is a wide variety of study types but common to them all is a measure of effect (lnor) together with its SE. Generate the forest plot using I-V weights with

```
. metan lnor se, eform  label(namevar=id) fixed
```

A random effects summary can be produced with

```
. metan lnor se, eform label(namevar=id) random
```

To stratify the analysis by study type, excluding the overall summary, try

```
. metan lnor se, eform label(namevar=id) random by(study_type) nooverall
```

To compare the fixed effects and random effects summaries, stratified by study type, add the option second(fixed). There does not seem to be much heterogeneity within each study type and therefore fixed and random effects summaries are very similar. The summaries for the different study types are also all close to 1.

The birth weight information was obtained from different sources, shown with

```
. tabulate bw_source
```

Stratifying by bw_source with

```
. sort bw_source id
. metan lnor se, eform by(bw_source)  label(namevar=id) random nooverall
```

shows that the results differ between type of information source, with studies with information from birth records giving a higher, and significant, summary effect.

To facilitate reading the plot, remove the boxes and the information on the weights with

```
. metan lnor se, eform by(bw_source)  label(namevar=id) random nooverall
    nobox nowt
```

We can investigate the heterogeneity across studies with different sources of birth weight information with metareg. Because metareg was written before Stata 11 it does not allow factor variables, but it is easy to produce the indicator variables for levels 2 and 3 of bw_source using the Stata 10 prefix xi: (see Section 15.6) as follows:

```
. xi: metareg lnor i.bw_source, wsse(se) eform
```

where wsse() is obligatory and contains the variable which records the within study SE. We can test whether the evidence from studies with data from parental or adult recall differs from that of studies with data from birth records with

```
. testparm _Ibw_source*
```

which gives a Wald test of 5.57, $p = 0.01$. See the help file for more options in metareg.

19.7 Funnel plots

A source of concern when meta-analyses are reported is that not all relevant evidence is included. One such source of selection is publication bias, where studies with significant effects are more likely to be published and then to be identified in systematic reviews. To assess this we can use a funnel plot, which is a scatterplot of the study effects against a measure of their precision. Studies with low precision will show a wide variation in effects while studies with high precision will show much less variation, leading to a plot which looks like an inverted funnel. As an example, try

```
. metafunnel  lnor se
```

An asymmetric distribution of points within the funnel shape would suggest the possibility of publication bias. In this case, among low precision studies (i.e. those with larger SE's), there seems to be a deficit of studies with negative effects which suggests that they did not make it into the meta analysis. This is purely a visual impression, but a statistical test can be carried out with the metabias command which computes the Egger test based on a weighted linear regression of the effects on their precision, as measured by the inverse of their standard errors. If the regression is flat there is no bias. Try

```
. metabias  lnor se ,graph egger
```

There does not seem to be any such bias.

19.8 Fixed or random effects?

The interpretation of results from a fixed effect or random effects meta-analysis is very different. For the first the pooled summary represents the common effect shared by all studies, in the second the pooled summary is the *average* of the separate study effects.

If we knew that each study had been conducted in the same way and on the same population, then a fixed effect summary would be appropriate. However, this is hardly ever the case especially when the studies are based on observational data. In general then, random effects pooled estimates are more appropriate.

If there is little variation across studies the choice is not so crucial, as the two approaches would give very similar results. If there is variation, the most crucial information to be drawn from the data is not their average but rather their source of variation. So in most settings, meta-regression should be the focus of the investigation and of the reported results.

Exercises

The data for these exercises comes from Harbord and Higgins [8] and concern a meta-analysis of 28 randomized controlled trials of various interventions aimed at lowering cholesterol and therefore lowering the risk of nonfatal myocardial infarction and ischemic heart disease (IHD) death. The dataset is called `chol.dta`.

1. Load the `chol` dataset and identify the number of treated and non-treated cases and the number of treated and non-treated non-cases. Use these numbers to produce a forest plot of the study-specific odds ratios for treatment without calculating the overall summary value. Is there evidence of heterogeneity between the studies?

2. Restricting the analyses to the studies in group 2 produce a forest plot and a fixed effect summary using Mantel-Haenszel weights. Produce the corresponding random effects summary and examine the between studies variance. Is there evidence of heterogeneity in this subgroup?

3. Calculate the fixed effect summary using inverse-variance weights. Are the three fixed effect summary values different?

4. Calculate the log odds ratio and its associated standard error for every study and then reproduce the summary OR for the studies in group 2 using the `metan` command with these two new variables. Which weights have you used?

5. Repeat this analysis but this time use all studies, stratifying by `group`. Add random effects summaries using the `second(...)` option. Examine the plot and also the group-specific tests for heterogeneity. What do you conclude?

6. The variable `cholreduc` holds the average reduction in cholesterol (mmol/l) achieved by the treatment. Plot `group` against `cholreduc`. What do you conclude? Plot the study-specific log odds ratios against `cholreduc`. Now use `metareg` to assess whether the heterogeneity across the trials can be at least partly explained by `cholreduc`.

164

Chapter 20

Exporting results

At some stage it will be necessary to export the results from your analyses to another application such as a word processor or LaTeX so that they can be published. A number of commands have been written by users which format the results from Stata commands to help in this process, and some of these are illustrated here.

20.1 Copy and paste

Following any Stata command, the results displayed in the results window can be highlighted using the mouse and then copied by right-clicking the mouse. In Microsoft Windows you will be offered the choice between *Copy Text* for pasting into a word processor, and *Copy Table* for pasting into a spreadsheet. As an example try

```
. use births, clear
. table sex hyp, c(mean bweight)
```

Now highlight the table in the results window using the left button of the mouse, right-click on the results window, and select *Copy Text*. Open a word processor, select a fixed width font such as Courier New, then select *Edit* and *Paste*. The table will now be pasted into the word processor. You should use the *Copy Table* option if you are pasting the table into a spreadsheet. This option copies the table as a tab-delimited file so that each number will paste into a separate cell.

There are many disadvantages to this method of exporting results: the outcome is quite crude, the process is error prone when copying many results, and it is tedious to repeat if the data change. It is much better to format the results first and then write them to a file which can be opened by a word processor or processed by LaTeX.

20.2   Formatting results for the screen

There is no general way of formatting the results from *any* Stata command, but a number of commands have been written by users, mainly for formatting the results from estimation commands. As an example of an estimation command, try

```
. regress bweight gestwks matage
```

We are mainly interested in those results relating to the parameters of the regression model, and to format these we shall first use the command `estout`, installed with

```
. ssc install estout, replace
```

Doing this also installs a number of other related commands, in particular `esttab`, which is a wrapper for `estout`, and `eststo`. These files are also included with the files which came with the book, but installing them from the SSC website makes sure you have the latest versions. To see what `esttab` does, try

```
. estimates clear
. regress bweight gestwks matage
. estimates store m1
. esttab m1
```

An alternative to `estimates store` is to use the command `eststo`:

```
. eststo clear
. eststo: regress bweight gestwks matage
. esttab
```

The `essto` command stores the estimates with the name `est1` and this is automatically picked up by the `esttab` command. This example shows the basic output from `esttab` but there are many options to improve this. We have chosen to display some of these using the do file `myest1.do` which you should run with

```
. pause on
. do myest1
```

Each example ends with a pause so you can inspect the output on the screen; to continue, type `q` and press *Enter*; to exit from the do file type **BREAK**. All of these examples use the estimates stored in `est1`, but it is also possible to combine the results for several models. After the second `eststo` the estimates are stored in `est2` and so on. The `esttab` automatically processes all the stored estimates unless specific ones are declared. Combining results is demonstrated with

```
. do myest2
```

The commands `eststo` and `esttab` can deal with factor variables, but it is necessary to use the `drop` option in `esttab` to avoid output referring to the baselines of the factor variables. First try

```
. eststo clear
. eststo: regress bweight i.hyp##i.sex
. esttab
```

to see the problem with baseline information. Now try

```
. esttab, drop(*b.*)
```

which drops the baseline information.

20.3 Formatting results for a word processor

Results from `esttab` can be written to either a tab delimited file or a rich text file.[1]
For example

```
. esttab est1 using myfile.tab, replace
```

writes to a tab delimited file. Open this file in a word processor and check its content.
An alternative is to create an `.rtf` file with

```
. esttab est1 using myfile.rtf, replace
```

and then to open this in a word processor. It is also possible to create `.csv` and `.html`
files. Files can be added to an existing file using the option `append`. To demonstrate
this try running the do file `myest3.do` with

```
. do myest3
```

20.4 Formatting results for LaTeX

LaTeXis a free mark-up language for producing documents which is widely used when
submitting papers for publication. The Stata journal is prepared using LaTeX, as is
this book. The most widely used versions are MikTex for Microsoft Windows and
TexLive for Unix and Mac OS, and these can be obtained from the comprehensive
tex archive network (CTAN) together with an introduction to using LaTeX. Even if
you have never used LaTeXbefore, the short account which follows may be of interest
as most of the work is done by `esttab`.

A LaTeXdocument has the following general form

```
\documentclass[12pt]{article}
\begin{document}

Stuff

\end{document}
```

---

[1]The Rich Text Format was developed by Microsoft for cross-platform document interchange.
Most word processors are able to read and write RTF documents.

There are several documentclasses, but `article` will be used here, with a 12pt font. To produce a `.tex` file with these two heading lines, plus a table in LATEXformat, followed by the final end line, try

```
. esttab est1 using myfile.tex, replace page
```

where the option `page` asks for the heading and end lines. Before this can be viewed it must be converted to `myfile.pdf` using `pdflatex` from your LATEXinstallation, and should then look like this in a pdf viewer:

	(1)
	bweight
gestwks	197.0***
	(22.38)
matage	0.0384
	(0.01)
_cons	-4490.4***
	(-11.79)
N	490

t statistics in parentheses
* $p < 0.05$, ** $p < 0.01$, *** $p < 0.001$

It is possible to add to an existing `.tex` file with the `append` option, as with an `.rtf` file, but the `page` option must be included after `append`.

20.5   Other commands for processing output

We have concentrated on `esttab` because it is relatively easy to use, and is very versatile, but there are a number of alternative commands which also have their following. Three of the most popular are `outreg`, `outreg2` and `parmest`, all of which can be installed with `ssc install`. The command `parmest` works by replacing the data in memory by the estimation results, which can then be processed using standard Stata commands. The command `outreg2` started as an extension of `outreg` but then diverged. It works in a similar way to `estout` by using a large number of options to shape the output in the desired form. It is included with the files which came with this book, but can also be installed with

```
. ssc install outreg2, replace
```

Try

```
. use births, clear
. regress bweight matage gestwks
. outreg2 using myfile, replace
. regress bweight gestwks
. outreg2 using myfile
```

The output ends up in a file called `myfile.txt` – to see what is in this file, click on the second blue *seeout*. You will see that each combination of an estimation command and an outreg command adds a new column to the file. The option `word` with the last `outreg2` command produces `myfile.rtf` instead of `myfile.txt`, and this can be opened in a word processor and incorporated in a report. The option `tex` with the last `outreg2` command produces `myfile.tex`. The option `nocons` with each `outreg2` command omits the constant term, and there are many other options for changing the appearance of the final result.

Exercises

There are no exercises for this chapter, but you might like to try to export some results to a word processor of your choice.

Chapter 21

How Stata is organized

In this chapter you will learn how to use the `adopath` command; how to update Stata over the internet; how to use the Stata FAQs; how to subscribe to the Statalist; how to install commands written by users; and where to find the *Stata Journal*.

21.1   Paths and programs

Stata does not come as a single monolithic program which the user is unable to modify. Instead the philosophy is to allow the user as much control as possible. There is a relatively small compiled binary file which carries out the task of organizing and interpreting the rest of the software, including data input, but most of the Stata commands come as independent files to which the user can gain access. These files are called *ado files*, which stands for *automatically loaded do files*. They have the extension `.ado`, so for example, the program code for the command `table` is in the file `table.ado`. There are several thousands of ado files which make up Stata, and they increase in number all the time.

Each Stata ado file itself consists of Stata commands. This is why the software takes only a small amount of space on the hard disk. If each command consisted of code for a stand-alone program, the package would be many times bigger. This is also what makes it possible for users to write simple programs for their own use. A new program may consist of only a few lines of other Stata commands, whereas a stand-alone version would be much larger and writing the code would require far greater programming skills.

An important command for understanding how Stata is organized is `adopath`. This reports the paths which Stata will search when you type a command. Try

```
. adopath
```

If you are using Stata under Microsoft Windows you should see something like this:

```
[1]   (UPDATES)    "C:\Program Files\Stata12\ado\updates/"
[2]   (BASE)       "C:\Program Files\Stata12\ado\base/"
[3]   (SITE)       "C:\Program Files\Stata12\ado\site/"
[4]                "."
[5]   (PERSONAL)   "C:\ado\personal/"
[6]   (PLUS)       "C:\ado\plus/"
[7]   (OLDPLACE)   "C:\ado/"
```

The paths are listed in the order in which they are searched. To find `table.ado`, Stata looks first in the **UPDATES** directory, to see whether the original `table.ado` has been updated. If it is not found there, Stata looks in the **BASE** directory, and so on, down the list. The entry `"."` stands for your working directory. Packages from the internet are installed in `C:\ado\plus/`. Note that Stata accepts either forward slash or backward slash in pathnames.

Additional paths can be added to the search list, as in

```
. adopath + C:\courses\ado/
```

which will add `C:\courses\ado/` to the search list. Similarly paths can be removed, most easily by number. For example

```
. adopath -3
```

will remove the **SITE** directory, and re-number the rest. It is sometimes useful to add a path to the start of the search list, to make sure that Stata looks there first. Try

```
. adopath ++ C:\courses\ado/
```

to add `C:\courses\ado/` at the start of the search list. These facilities are useful because Stata can only find commands which are in directories on the **adopath**.

To find out in which directory a particular command, such as `table`, has been found, try

```
. which table
```

and you should see that `table.ado` is in the `...\ado\base\t` directory, while

```
. which cdfplot
```

should show that `cdfplot.ado` is in the `...\ado\plus\c` directory.

21.2 Updating Stata

The way Stata is organized, as a set of interlinked programs, means that it is important to update the package regularly. Fortunately, provided you have a connection to the internet, and permission to write to the Stata directory, there is a very simple way of updating Stata over the internet. The command

```
. update query
```

will report the current state of your system, and advise whether it needs updating. In response to the advice you can type

```
. update all
```

For details of how to proceed if you don't have permission to write to the Stata directory, see the *Getting Started Guide* in the documentation.

21.3 The Stata Journal

The *Stata Journal* publishes peer-reviewed papers together with shorter notes or comments, regular columns, book reviews and other material of interest to Stata users. For information on the journal, including instructions for authors, see

```
http://www.stata-journal.com
```

and for information on how to obtain copies see

```
http://www.stata.com/bookstore/sj.html
```

When papers in the journal describe new commands the ado files for these can be freely downloaded (see below). Prior to the *Stata Journal*, new commands were published in the *Stata Technical Bulletin* (STB), and these commands are still available from the Stata website.

21.4 User-written commands

User-written commands are supplied without any guarantee that they will work properly, but in fact are usually of a high standard. Finding a user–written command usually starts with a keyword search to see whether commands relevant to a particular application exist. For example, click on *Help*, then *Search*, then check *Search documentation and FAQs*, and type `smr` in the box provided. The search on `smr` first provides commands which are included in Stata, such as `dstdize`. These are indicated by [U] for User's Guide, [R] for the Base Reference, or something like [ST] which refers to the section on survival time in the documentation. Any relevant commands which have been published by the SJ (or STB) follow. Clicking on the blue code corresponding to the command puts you in a position to install. For example, clicking on `sg29.1` will bring you to a page showing which files are in the package `smrby`, and you can then install them by clicking on *click here to install*. The `ado` and `hlp` files will go in the PLUS directory, first checking that they is not already installed. If they is, and the new version is different, no action is taken, unless you ask for it to be replaced. You can also get any ancillary files (usually data files) which will go into your current working directory.

To widen the search you can click on *Search net resources* This will search a number of websites, including the SSC-IDEAS website, which contains a wealth of material. Providing you know the name of a command you can install it directly from the SSC website, along with the help file, with

```
. ssc install command_name
```

For further details on the use of `ssc` try

```
. help ssc
```

What all of the these searches are looking for is Stata packages: these are collections of files – typically `.ado` and `.hlp` files – which provide a new feature in Stata. In general, the commands

```
. net from        (the source URL)
. net install     (the name of the package)
. net get         (the name of the package)
```

will work for any package for which you know the URL. The `net install` installs the ado files while the `net get` loads any ancillary files. The `net from` command is also useful for installing packages from your own hard disk or CD-ROM (see Chapter 0). To update commands written by users, which you have previously loaded, try

```
. adoupdate
```

21.5   The Statalist

A useful resource for both beginners and experienced users of Stata is the Statalist, which is a listserver, and distributes messages to all subscribers. Although independent of Stata Corporation, the list is carefully monitored by the Corporation for problems with the current version of Stata and suggestions for the next release. It is recommended that all users join the list, which is easily done by sending the message "subscribe statalist" to

```
majordomo@hsphsun2.harvard.edu
```

To unsubscribe, send the message "unsubscribe statalist". To send a message to the list, send it to

```
statalist@hsphsun2.harvard.edu
```

but if it is a request for help, you are strongly advised to check the documentation, and to read the FAQs (Frequently Asked Questions) at the Stata website before doing this. These are kept at

```
http://www.stata.com/support/faqs
```

and are a very useful source of information.

21.6   Other sources of help

The main source of information about Stata is the documentation. This is an excellent source of information about both Stata and statistics. In addition Stata Corporation and Timberlake Consultants offer courses over the internet. See `www.stata.com` and `www.timberlake.co.uk` for details of dates and prices.

Stata has a technical support group which will sort out any problems for registered users, but before contacting them you are advised to check the FAQs and other sources of documentation. See the Stata webpage, under *User Support* and *Technical Support* for more details. A number of useful books for learning more about statistics while using Stata have been published. See the Stata webpage under *Bookstore* for more details. The Stata community is generous with its help. There are many sources of written material in addition to those mentioned above, but one in particular is

`http://www.ats.ucla.edu/stat/stata`

Bibliography

[1] E. Christensen, J. Neuberger, J. Crowe, D.G. Altman, H. Popper, B. Portmann, D. Doniach, L. Raneck, N. Tygtrup, and R. Williams. Beneficial effect of aza-thioprine and prediction of prognosis in primary biliary cirrhosis. Final results of an international trial. *Gastroenterology*, 89:1084–1091, 1985.

[2] D.G. Clayton and M. Hills. *Statistical Models in Epidemiology*. Oxford University Press, Oxford, 1993.

[3] M Cleves, W. G. Gould, and R. Guttierez. *An Introduction to Survival Analysis using Stata, Revised Edition*. Stata Press, College Station, TX, USA, 2004.

[4] G.A. Colditz, T.F. Brewer, and et. al. Berkey, C.S. Efficacy of bcg vaccine in the prevention of tuberculosis: meta-analysis of the published literature. *Journal American Medical Association*, 271:688–702, 1994.

[5] N.J. Cox. Speaking Stata: How to repeat yourself without going mad. *The Stata Journal*, 1:86–97, 2001.

[6] I. dos Santos Silva, B. L. De Stavola, Collaborative Group on Pre-Natal Risk Factors, and Subsequent Risk of Breast Cancer. Birth size and breast cancer risk: Re-analysis of individual participant data from 32 studies. *PLoS Med*, 5:e193. doi:10.1371/journal.pmed.0050193, 2008.

[7] W.A. Guy. *Journal of the Royal Statistical Society*, 6:197–211, 1843.

[8] R.M. Harbord and J.P.T. Higgins. Meta-regression in Stata. *Stata Journal*, 8(4):493–519, 2008.

[9] N. Mantel and W. Haenszel. Statistical aspects of the analysis of data from retrospective studies. *Journal of the National Cancer Institute*, 22:719–748, 1959.

[10] K. Molbak and T. Hald. An outbreak of *salmonella* typhimurium in the county of Funen during late summer. A case-control study. *Ugeskr Laeger*, 159:5372–7, 1997.

[11] J.N. Morris, J.W. Marr, and D.G. Clayton. Diet and heart: a postscript. *British Medical Journal*, 19 November(2):1307–14, 1977.

[12] H. Putter, M. Fiocco, and R.B. Geskus. Tutorial in biostatistics: Competing risks and multi-state models. *Statistics in Medicine*, 26(11):2389–430, 2007.

[13] K.J. Rothman. *Modern Epidemiology*. Little, Brown, and Company, Boston, 1986.

[14] J. Sterne. *Meta-analysis In Stata: An Updated Collection From The Stata Journal*. Stata Press, 2009.

Index